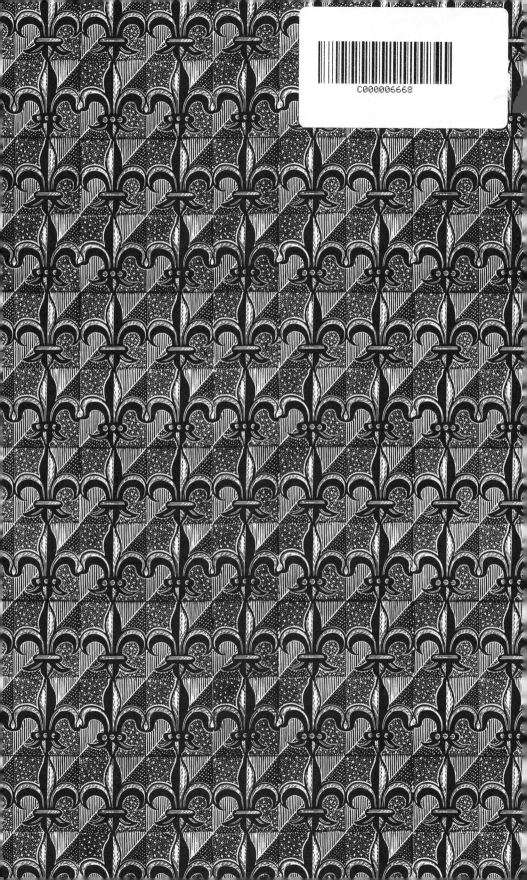

The Old Man
and Me

Also by Allan Prior

NOVELS

A Flame In The Air
The Joy Ride
The One-Eyed Monster
One Away
The Interrogators
The Operators
The Loving Cup
The Contract
Paradiso

Affair
Never Been Kissed In The Same Place
   Twice
Theatre ('A Cast of Stars' in USA)
The Big March
Her Majesty's Hit Man
The Charmer
Fuhrer

SOME TELEVISION PLAYS

Z Cars
Softly, Softly
The One-Eyed Monster
The Charmer
The Bookie Trilogy

A Perfect Hero
The Golden Mile Trilogy
Moonstrike
Romany Rye: George Borrow
Rob Roy MacGregor

SOME PLAYS FOR RADIO

Worker In The Dawn: a Portrait of George Gissing
Alias Baron Corvo: a Portrait of Frederick Rolfe
The Running Man: a Portrait of W. T. Stead
Nosey: a Portrait of the Duke of Wellington
Fuhrer: a Portrait of Adolf Hitler

STAGE

The West Pier (from a novel by Patrick Hamilton)

The
Old Man
and Me

Allan Prior

SINCLAIR-STEVENSON

First published in Great Britain in 1994
by Sinclair-Stevenson
an imprint of Reed Consumer Books Ltd
Michelin House, 81 Fulham Road, London SW3 6RB
and Auckland, Melbourne, Singapore and Toronto

A CIP catalogue record for this book is available
at the British Library

ISBN 1 85619 380 2

Phototypeset by Intype, London
Printed and bound in Great Britain
by Clays Ltd, St Ives PLC

For My Children
and Their Children

Acknowledgements

The author and publishers are grateful for permission to reproduce words from songs as follows:

'When the Red, Red Robin Comes Bob, Bob, Bobbin' Along' (p. 105), words and music by Harry Woods © 1926, Bourne Co, USA. Reproduced by permission of Francis Day and Hunter Ltd, London WC2H oEA.

'Red Sails in the Sunset' (p. 137), music by Hugh Williams and words by Jimmy Kennedy © 1935. Reproduced by permission of Peter Maurice Music Co Ltd, London WC2H oEA.

'Nellie Dean' (p. 139), words and music by Harry Armstrong © 1905, M Witmark and Sons, USA. Reproduced by permission of B Feldman and Co Ltd, London WC2H oEA.

'The Washing on the Siegfried Line' (p. 171), words and music by Michael Carr and Jimmy Kennedy © 1939. Reproduced by permission of Peter Maurice Music Co Ltd, London WC2H oEA.

Contents

The Warrant

The Detective stood at the front door. He said, 'Is Percy in?'

I didn't know he was a Detective then. I only found out later. He was, however, the kind of man who might call at the house asking for the Old Man. Masculine, impatient, certain of who he was, often smoking a cigarette and wearing a hat, as the Detective was.

I called, 'There's a gentleman here to see you.'

The Old Man appeared in the hall, carrying the Racing Paper. He was, as always, clean-shaven, wearing a hard white collar and his regimental tie, that of the Northumberland Fusiliers. His hair was still dark and glossy then, and his magnificent teeth showed when he smiled. He broke brazil nuts with those teeth as a Christmas trick. He was smiling now and extending his hand.

'Jack, come in, come in.'

The Detective entered, taking off his trilby. The Old Man ushered him into the living room.

The Detective stood and looked round the room, which was large for a suburban house and difficult to heat, which is why the Old Man had got it at a reasonable rent. When he paid it.

'Nice place, Percy.'

The room was full of new furniture on the HP. The Old Man owed on that as well.

'Not bad, Jack.'

The Old Man, without asking, got a bottle of whisky and two tumblers from the sideboard and poured two liberal measures, a particularly large one for the Detective. The Old Man was not a drinker. Gambling was his vice, his pleasure and his life.

'Good health,' said the Old Man, raising his glass.

'Very best, Percy,' said the Detective, sipping and nodding to the quality of the whisky. They sat in silence for a long moment, as the clock ticked on the mantelpiece.

The Old Man always had a good timepiece. He had to know if he was in time to get a bet on.

'Well,' said the Old Man, 'what brings you to this part of the world, Jack?'

By that he meant Blackpool. The Detective, from his Geordie sing-song, was from Newcastle, which the Old Man had left a year before. Blackpool was booming, but Tyneside was under the looming blight of the Depression. My sister Peggy used to say that if the Old Man paid all his gambling debts the Depression would lift off Tyneside.

The Detective had not replied directly to the Old Man's question. Instead, he took from the inside of his jacket a large, official-looking envelope.

'I have a warrant for you, Percy.'

The Detective's voice was apologetic.

But the Old Man simply nodded imperturbably. 'Can I have a look at it?' he asked.

'Of course you can, it's for you. I had a hell of a job finding you. Nobody in Newcastle knew where you'd gone.'

The Old Man took and opened out the document, which seemed to be part-typed and part-handwritten, and perused it with a practised eye.

'This is for Rates for the Shop in Clayton Street.'

The Detective drank his whisky and nodded. He said nothing.

'That Shop has nothing to do with me, Jack. It's Marthaann's Shop and I believe she's closed it now.'

Marthaann was my mother. She was always opening and closing shops in the Depression.

The Detective confirmed that with another nod. 'But it's your name on the document. She put the whole thing in your name.'

'Only,' said the Old Man, mildly, 'because they wouldn't rent it to her since she was a woman.'

'You know that and I know that,' said the Detective. 'The County Court don't care about that.'

'No,' said the Old Man, 'I don't suppose they do.'

The clock on the mantelpiece chimed the hour. The Old Man stirred and looked at it. I wondered what he had backed in the last Race of the day.

'It's for a hundred pound, Percy,' said the Detective. 'I don't suppose you have it?'

'A hundred?' The Old Man looked at the document. 'So it is. I didn't know it was for as much as that.'

'Marthaann's opened another shop,' said the Detective. 'It's in Percy Street.'

'That's always been hers,' the Old Man said. 'It belonged to her father, Isaac. It's the only shop she's ever had that shows a profit. She only opens it when she's pushed.'

'Then,' said the Detective, 'she must be pushed.'

The Old Man got up and poured two more measures of

whisky. He whistled noiselessly through his teeth, which meant that he was thinking. He took from his pocket a twenty-pack of Churchman's and offered one to the Detective, who accepted it with a nod of approval. The Detective smoked Woodbines. The Old Man had never smoked Woodbines in his life, not even in the Trenches.

The two men lit up and inhaled. They did not seem to notice my presence. Those were different days. You hung as you grew then.

'What,' said the Old Man absently, 'is the form, Jack?'

The Detective surveyed his Churchman's, courteously. 'If you haven't got the hundred I have to take you back to Newcastle with me.' He added, in apology, 'They're very hot on Rates, Percy. You know that.'

'Well,' said the Old Man. 'It's really down to Marthaann.'

The Detective nodded. 'Just the same.'

'I know,' said the Old Man. 'I know. When do you go back to Newcastle? You can't do it tonight.'

'No,' said the Detective. 'I'll have to get a bed-and-break-fast and go back on the ten o'clock in the morning.'

'Don't bother with a B-and-B,' said the Old Man. 'Stay at the Palatine Hotel. It's opposite the railway station.'

'Won't run to it,' the Detective said. 'It'll be pounds-ten in a place like that.'

'Not it!' The Old Man stood up and shot his cuffs, which were as usual impeccable. The shoes shone, too. The suit, once very good, no longer was. The Old Man always said if your hair, collar and tie and shoes were good, nobody noticed anything else. As in so many other things, he was wrong.

The Old Man put on his hat, an expensive grey Woodrow. 'I'll walk to the tram with you, Jack. I'll give the manager of

4

the Palatine a ring from the box at the corner. I think you'll find you'll be all right.'

The Detective stood up heavily, swallowing the last of his whisky in a gulp. 'Will you have the hundred for me?'

'What time does your train go?'

'Ten o'clock sharp.'

The Old Man temporised. 'Then I'll see you at the barrier at a quarter-to-ten.'

'You'll have it, for sure?' The Detective looked studiously at the carpet, which was new and not paid for. 'I don't have anything to worry about?'

'I have to see Edwards,' said the Old Man.

'I had heard he was here,' admitted the Detective. 'What's he doing, your brother?'

'Making a Book at the Dogs.' The Old Man puffed on his cigarette. They were a social habit with him, like the drinking. He did not inhale deeply, as the Detective did. And he held the cigarette between his first two fingers, not cradled in his hand as the Detective did. A gentleman always held his cigarette that way, the Old Man said.

'Doing all right?' asked the Detective.

'He was living at the Metropole in St Anne's for a while,' said the Old Man. 'Never went to bed with less than two women in those days.'

'He was always in the money,' the Detective conceded. 'Always.'

'He has the gift,' said the Old Man. 'He got married last year.'

'Never!' said the Detective, in genuine surprise. 'What age will he be now?'

'Sixty-one,' said the Old Man. He was fifty himself.

'Well then, if you're seeing him, give him my best.' The Detective followed the Old Man out of the house.

At the door, the Old Man said in a low voice, 'Go and see if Ray Barry has anything for me, will you? Then come on to the tram-stop.'

Ray Barry, the Bookmaker, known to the neighbourhood as Razz, had nothing for the Old Man, he informed me, without admitting me to his house. He was a street-bookie. Many years later, at the Old Man's funeral, to which a surprising number of people turned up, I asked Razz if he had ever known the Old Man back a winner. 'Many and many a dozen,' he had conceded, blowing his nose. 'Never the last one.'

Razz had smiled then as he smiled now, as most people smiled when they spoke of the Old Man. Smiled and shook their heads. I thanked him and turned to go. 'I hear you're Top of the Class again. Keep it up, lad!'

The Old Man, whose only comment to me on my scholastic success, such as it was, was an absent 'I don't know how you do it', was forever boasting about me to his racing friends. Like him, they could not understand it and wondered what it was for.

Marthaann had a very high intelligence, but her Father, the tycoon Isaac, had taken her away from school and put her in one of his shops at fourteen years of age. She was only a woman and would get married.

As it turned out, the experience of the shops had given her a life, once he had gone, drinking the seventeen shops away, shop by shop.

When I got to the tram-stop, the Old Man was coming out of the telephone booth. The Detective was waiting. The Old Man said, 'Ask for Mister Entwhistle. Nothing to pay.'

The Detective looked pleased. 'You're sure, Percy?'

'Positive.'

The Detective unhappily shook the Old Man's hand. 'See you tomorrow morning, Percy.'

'As ever was, Jack,' said the Old Man.

'I hope you have the hundred with you,' said the Detective. 'It's a lot of money, Percy.'

'It is,' said the Old Man.

It was. About two thousand pounds in today's money. And a lot harder to get, then.

The Detective got on the tram and it rattled away towards the Town. The 'Town' was the Golden Mile and the Tower and the visitors and the cinemas and a lot of noise and bustle.

'I like Blackpool, it's all push and shove,' a Jewish man in Lyon's Café had said to my Sister after pricing her rings for her. He had taken her for Jewish, as many did. Her standard reply was, 'Well, I'm not, but my Grandfather was called Isaac and he had a big nose.'

'You can always tell,' the Jewish man had said.

I asked the Old Man, 'What now?'

'I'm thinking,' said the Old Man.

'Edwards will be in now,' I said, impatiently. I did not fancy the idea of the Old Man going to jail. How would I explain it at my new school? He did not seem concerned. 'Yes, we'll have to go and see Edwards, nothing else for it.'

'Edwards' was called that because when *his* Father had died, having lost all his money in a Music Hall venture, he had gone to his Bookmaker and asked, 'Tell me how to become a Bookie!'

The Bookie, aghast, had said, 'You can't be a Bookie, Sir, you're a gentleman.'

'Gentleman be buggered,' said Edwards. 'I'm broke!'

His Bookmaker made a face. 'You'll have to change your name. You can't use your Father's, it wouldn't be right, would it?'

So he had become 'Edwards', and was always so addressed, even when he won the British (Amateur) Gentleman's Snooker Title. Everybody in the Racing Game knew him.

The Old Man and I made our way to his house on the next tram, a tuppeny ride, half-price for under-fourteens. I was over fourteen but paid half. To the Old Man's horror, Edwards was not in. Instead, 'that fokkin Ogre', as the Old Man called Edwards' wife Dorothy (under his breath), opened the door. She was properly cautious because Edwards was a street-bookie (as most were, then) and an accounts-bookie as well.

Sometimes, the Police raided a Bookie's premises in the hope of finding punters present, which was illegal.

Edwards never personally collected bets in streets or bars, which was also illegal, but had a collection of decrepit old Runners working for him, using clock-bags. These small leather cases had a built-in clock that stopped when they were shut, that is, before the Race in question was run: a necessary precaution in a very inventive business.

The work was risky, as the police had to make arrests from time to time. Edwards never took that risk.

'The man,' the Old Man would say, 'is an arrant fokkin coward!'

The Old Man never knew he was swearing or that he was being overheard. These remarks were a private communion with himself, and he was astonished if anybody took him up on them. He swore in the army fashion, as punctuation.

The Ogre Dorothy said, 'He's gone to the Grand Hotel to get in an hour's practice on the table. He has a money match coming up. It's no use asking me who against or how much for, because he never tells me anything. That's where you'll find him if you want him.'

She did not invite us into the large house, which doubled as an office. Two clerks took the telephone-bets from punters who had accounts with Edwards. Dorothy had married Edwards when he had fallen ill the previous winter. He had taught her the Business. 'I'm not surprised you fell ill,' Dorothy had told him, at his bedside. 'I believe you've been living a disgraceful life at the Metropole in St Anne's. That'll have to stop.'

'It has stopped, Pig,' said Edwards, in bed in his thick flannel pyjamas, a stag at bay. He had had an affair with Dorothy many years before, when she was a young and attractive dancer in one of George Edwardes' Companies. Now, he suddenly needed money, and she had it.

'There's only one condition,' she had said.

'Marriage, Pig, I suppose?' Nobody knew why he called her Pig.

Thus, she was, as the Old Man said, 'Ensconced', in Edwards' life. Ensconced was the Old Man's kind of word, the family's kind of word.

The Old Man and his Brothers had obtained a good education, for the times. They knew their Dickens and Shakespeare, and many, many quotations from famous politicians and soldiers. In those days it was enough to distinguish a gentleman from a worker.

There were a thousand other ways, of course.

One was to raise your hat to a lady as you retreated, and this the Old Man now did.

'I hear you're top,' called my Aunt Dorothy.

'Yes,' I said.

9

'Keep it up,' she warned me. Everything she said was a warning. She was known in the family as Frosty Face.

The Old Man could not get over the fact that my education cost nothing, but Aunt Dorothy, whose Father had been a London taxi-driver, had known nobody in her family who had paid a penny for any education, with the result, the Old Man said, that none of them could spell cat.

Leaving the house, the Old Man showed concern for the first time. 'That's a pity. I don't know how much money Edwards will have on him.'

I knew he meant that any money he managed to 'extract' (his word) from Edwards would have to be without Dorothy having knowledge of it. So, to the Grand Hotel, a short walk, where we found Edwards alone on one of the tables in the Billiard-room, patiently potting reds. He greeted us courteously (he was always mild and unsurprisable) and led, as he always had, a life of total, benign selfishness.

He was generous, however, and had never been known to refuse a request, except, as the Old Man said, when he didn't have it.

That turned out to be the case now.

'I haven't got a hundred on me, Percy.' Edwards potted a difficult red, putting side on it so that it came back behind the black. He had made many centuries in his time, and never played except for money. He had beaten a Jewish professional for a hundred pounds a side at the age of nineteen. 'Not just a professional,' the Old Man had recounted to me: 'A *Jewish* professional!'

That seemed to make the success even more surprising, and reflected well on Edwards, who bore his successes modestly. His failures, too. He was immensely popular on and off the race-tracks, with men and women both, the women only more so.

Now, he pondered, his silvery-gold hair short and brilliantined, the Savile Row suit he always wore (he went up to Town for them) fitting him closely, as was the fashion then. 'Let me finish this frame. I'm playing the Butcher tomorrow night.'

The Butcher was a local Nobody who could shop a ball or two, and who thought because Edwards was sixty years old he was a pushover, said the Old Man. He was in for a surprise then? I hazarded. The Old Man whispered, 'Well, Edwards' eyes are going . . . I wouldn't like to have a bet on it.'

An amazing statement from the Old Man, who would bet on two flies on a window-pane. On which one took off first.

'How much are they playing for?' I asked.

The Old Man didn't know.

Edwards put his cue in his tin case locked to the wall. 'If you want the money for tomorrow morning, then it's no use me going back to the office and arguing with Dorothy. I think we'd better go and see Joe Hyams.'

We caught yet another tram, to the North Pier this time.

It was now seven o'clock, but Joe Hyams was open for business. A sign above his office, which was up some dark, linoleum-covered stairs, read: JOE HYAMS MONEY LENT WITHOUT COLLATERAL.

Joe Hyams was a fat, cheerful man in his shirtsleeves. His office was sparsely furnished and lit by a single electric bulb. There was a large iron safe behind him. On the table was a bottle of whisky and two cups. He poured whisky into both cups and put them in front of Edwards and the Old Man.

Edwards said, mildly, 'Joe, I believe you lend money without collateral?'

The three men laughed loudly at that. Their laughter went on for a long time. Finally Joe Hyams wiped his eyes and said, 'What can I do for you?'

He did not look at the Old Man, whose credit-worthiness, it occurred to me, he must have known to a T, as people said then. Well, I knew it and I was only fourteen.

'It's a hundred Percy has to have.' Edwards looked out of the window at the visitors in their Kiss Me Quick paper hats. 'He has to have it now. I'll send somebody up with it for you tomorrow noonish.'

Joe Hyams pursed his lips. 'The loan is to you, not Percy.'

It was a statement. Edwards looked pained but inclined his head. 'Of course.'

Joe Hyams opened his huge safe-door and reached inside. He grasped a bundle of bank-notes, some of them the large flimsies (fivers and tenners) and some the old green One Pound notes. He riffled through them expertly and slipped them in a used envelope. 'Exactly one hundred. Shall we say a hundred, and five quid vigorish?'

'Very kind of you, Joe,' said Edwards. 'Helped me a lot, that.'

Joe Hyams looked pleased. Edwards had that effect on everybody. It came, as the Old Man said, from having a Rich Father. Edwards had never wanted for anything so he never felt poor. The Old Man had been born later and was only fifteen when the money went. It made a difference, obviously. Perhaps it was *the* difference. Nowadays people might say that sort of thing, but not then.

'Young fella going in the Game?' asked Joe Hyams, noticing me for the first time, now business was over.

'I doubt it. Top of the form,' said the Old Man.

'Stick in, Son,' said Joe Hyams. 'Don't finish up like us bloody lot, eh?'

The three men all laughed again, and then we were out of the office and the last gold of the dying sun was going down into the Irish Sea. Blackpool was the only place in England, the Old Man said, where you can see the sun set twice: once from the Promenade and then again from the top of the Tower, if you got in the next lift.

'Thanks, I'll let you have it back as soon as I can!' called the Old Man.

But Edwards was already boarding a tram.

'Will you be coming back home?' I asked the Old Man.

The word home caused a frown to appear on his face. He was a free spirit and home, any home, was a constraint. There was no excitement there.

'No, I have a bit of business, Son. I'll see you later.'

The Old Man kept money in many different pockets, a precaution in case he got 'dipped' at the Race-track. Now, he silently handed me a florin from out of his top left waistcoat pocket. I got on the tram wondering how it would all pan out, apprehensive that the Old Man might get into a card game and lose the money before the morning came and the fateful meeting with the Detective.

The meeting took place exactly as arranged. The Detective was standing in a cloud of steam from the waiting engine, and was consulting his steel timepiece when the Old Man arrived.

'By Christ, Percy, you've cut it fine! It goes in five minutes.'

'Did they look after you at the Palatine?'

'They did, in every way.' The Detective breathed heavily. 'Did you get the money?'

The Old Man sighed. 'No.'

'Ohmigod. You'll have to come with me then!'

'Only half of it. Fifty quid.'

'Fifty quid's no good! The Warrant's for a hundred!'

The Old Man pondered. The train guard blew his whistle. The Detective stood, shaking his head, a Woodbine in his mouth.

The Old Man handed him an envelope. 'There's fifty in there. Put it in your back pocket. You couldn't find me.'

The Detective hesitated a long moment.

The train guard blew his whistle again.

'By Christ, I never clapped my bloody eyes on you,' said the Detective, shook hands with the Old Man, and got on the train.

The Old Man lost the fifty pounds at the Dogs that night.

Marthaann

Marthaann married the Old Man when she was sixteen.

He was twenty-three and working as a barman in the old King's Head public house in Newcastle-on-Tyne at the time. The King's Head was the smallest pub in Newcastle, having only two barmen, the Old Man and Ted Bland, an elderly ex-seaman who had sailed Round the Horn three times on the old wind-jammers. Men came in for a pint, the Old Man said, simply to watch himself and Ted Bland work. 'There was so little room behind the bar,' said the Old Man, 'we were like a couple of ballet-dancers. We served two hundred pints a day and never spilled a drop.' The Old Man may have seen a hundred 'Light' Operas (his favourite being *Traviata*) but I doubt he ever went to the ballet.

He added, 'If no customer started a fight on a Saturday night Ted Bland would start one himself. When it began Ted Bland would throw the offender out into the street and if he was foolish enough to return for more, Ted would hold the two doors open, stun him with the first and knock him out with the second.'

Then the Old Man would blow a police-whistle and four members of the City Police would arrive, take speedy refreshment (if time allowed) and cart the dazed and bloody unfortunate away to the cells in Newgate Street. If the offender was still fighting, the policemen took an arm or a leg each and carried him, face down. If he still struggled, they 'dipped' his face, and the soft parts of his body, on the cobblestones. It was called a Frog March.

A locally-known troublemaker was detained that way one particularly noisy Saturday night. He wore a barred jersey, and was called Smellie, and he smashed up the bar and had Ted Bland at full exertion. The Police four-handed him out of it, calling out to the Old Man, 'We're preferring charges against this bastard. You'll have to come along as witness, Percy.'

So the Old Man, in his long barman's white apron, followed the Police unhappily (Smellie had a notoriously long memory) as they dipped Smellie more often than was absolutely necessary on their way to the Nick. Here, the Station Sergeant, an oldish man eating his supper sandwiches, surveyed Smellie without enthusiasm.

'Yer in it agen, are yer, yer big berk,' was his greeting.

Smellie, in reply, called the Station Sergeant all the names he could lay his tongue to. The Station Sergeant seemed not to hear him as he laboriously laid aside his supper and wrote down, with excruciating care, the charges being preferred.

All the time Smellie swore at him.

'I must admit I never heard a fellow swear so fluently,' admitted the Old Man, keeping well to the back of Smellie. 'For an uneducated man, that is.'

'Take him down,' said the Station Sergeant, at last.

Two of the policemen (and they were all six feet tall then, and broad of beam) took Smellie to the stone stairs leading down to the cells.

There, unaccountably, they let go of his arms.

Smellie stood there on the top step, free, bemused.

Only for a moment.

For the Station Sergeant was by now but a pace behind him. And his highly polished size ten boot struck Smellie up the backside.

The Old Man said, 'The man went down those stairs like a sack of coal.'

It was such incidents and such places that gave the Old Man a rich early experience of life. The alternative to working in the bars was clerking on a high stool in some office, and he'd tried that. There was freedom in the bars, despite the long hours and hard work (six in the morning until midnight, with a couple of hours off in the afternoons), that suited his nature. Nobody in the bars frowned if you had a bet on a horse. Indeed, they were surprised if you didn't. There was also a lot of silver and copper flying around, and with sleight of hand some of it stuck. The wages were nothing. Twenty-four bob and what you could make, that was the form.

On it, the Old Man lived in lodgings in Percy Street. One room he shared with his brother Frank, a young clerk. It was a carefree life, if not one he had expected. The family had had money but it had gone at a stroke with his Father's bankruptcy. His Father and Mother were dead, the family house sold, relatives too fussy, faraway and Methody for his tastes. He worked all week, had a lie-in one day only, ate plenty and well, slept sound and, as he put it, did not have a care in the fokkin world.

Until he met Marthaann Henderson.

Isaac Henderson, the Prawn King, owned and lived above his shop, opposite the King's Head public house. Since he had no licence, many of his customers carried drink across the busy street, into his Prawn Shop. Along his marble counters stood sixteen girls, Marthaann amongst them, each with an oyster-knife in hand, opening prawns, crabs, lobsters and oysters from noon until midnight. You could sit at any of his marble-topped tables in the restaurant at the back and eat a fourpenny or sixpenny crab of your choice; brown bread and butter, cut thick from an Edinburgh loaf, a penny extra. Or oysters at seasonal rate but never above a penny each. Or prawns (of the Dublin Bay variety) sometimes mistakenly called langoustines or even 'little lobsters'. These were the bedrock of my grandfather Isaac's trade. The family story was that he had seen his first prawns lying discarded amongst the fish, in the nets on the North Shields Quayside. He had asked the fisherman if they were good eating. The fisherman said, 'Just cook them for twenty minutes in brine.'

'Can I take a few in me cap?' asked Isaac Henderson, a true Lowland Scot.

'Take as many as ye like, man!'

Now, he had seventeen shops all over the North of England, selling the pink, succulent crustaceans. 'The man,' his Son-in-law reported, 'was a magnificent shopman. Unfortunately, also a brutal and ignorant old fellow, but possessed of a form of low cunning doing justice for intelligence.'

'Harsh judgement?' I offered.

'The description is Lord Elton's, not mine. However, it is singularly apt,' said the Old Man.

Isaac Henderson was certainly a big man. Seventeen stones of bone and muscle. Large moustache and black cowlick hair. It was said he could lift a barrel of prawns on to his fish-shop counter without effort and that nobody on the Fish Quay at North Shields was as strong as he was, no fisherman or filleter or fish-humper.

He was also, as he often boasted, as high in the Masonic Order as a man could go without being of Royal Blood. He was a member of fourteen lodges, many of them Temperance, for he did not take, in the Nonconformist fashion, to drink or women until he was fifty.

The Old Man was a member of but one Masonic Lodge and that was because it was the only place in Blackpool where you could get a drink, a game of billiards or a bet on during the afternoon. The Old Man was a Lewis, his dead father having been a Freemason.

It was into Isaac's family shop and station that the Old Man married. Or rather he didn't.

Isaac was reportedly incandescent with rage (as they say nowadays) to hear that his youngest, prettiest daughter was pregnant, and only the pressure of family and public opinion brought him to acknowledge that the most prudent course was to 'let them get on with it', and to give way to the marriage, which (disgracefully, for the time) was to take place in a Register Office.

It never, apparently, occurred to the Old Man to take flight.

One was, if not exactly a gentleman, at least not a total rotter. 'Married the bloody woman, didn't I?' he was to declare plaintively, when criticised years later.

The Old Man was quite simply not marriage material.

Yet his bride was a catch. The bouncy, dark-haired daughter of a wealthy man. A bright girl, too, sent home from school at fourteen with the message, 'We can't teach Marthaann any more. She should go to a College.'

'Nonsense,' said Isaac, and put her in the shop. Under his paternal eye, right in the middle of the city.

Now this. Never mind, the Good Lord sent for you to be tried. And the Good Lord was never far away. Perched, in fact, on the very clouds above his head. And All Seeing. As he himself often said, 'I never did a wrong thing but the Good Lord didn't punish me right afterwards.' Almost daily he proudly boasted, 'I never go to my bed without I read a verse of the Good Book.'

To which the Old Man added, under his breath, 'Drunk or sober.'

To the Old Man, Isaac made his proposition.

'Come into the business, Percy, and I'll give you a Shop.'

'The *fish* business?'

'That's what I do, isn't it?'

'But I don't know anything about it, Mr Henderson.'

'Isaac!'

'Isaac. I don't *know* the business, Isaac.'

The Old Man did not add his fervent plea: nor do I fokkin want to. Instead, he temporised. 'Would I own the shop?'

'Own it?' Isaac was shocked. 'Of course you wouldn't own it. You'd manage it. For me.'

'I see.' The Old Man surveyed the shop, the thousands of crustaceans piled high in the shop window, the girls' knives flashing in the gaslight. It seemed like a prison-yard to him. After all, he'd *married* Marthaann. 'I have prospects at the pub, Isaac.'

'What prospects? Head Barman in ten years' time?' Isaac took him by the shoulder. 'I wouldn't have let you marry Marthaann if I didn't know you came from good stock. Edward Prior was a gentleman, even if he had no business sense whatever. The idea of building a Music Hall in the middle of Newcastle!'

The Old Man said, 'It's full every night.'

Isaac shook his head. 'But it isn't *yours*, is it? Sold it to Moss, didn't he?'

'The Plans, yes. And paid seventeen shillings and sixpence in the pound when he went Bank.'

Isaac squeezed the Old Man's shoulder. 'There you are! Seventeen and sixpence in the pound! I'd have run to China rather than pay my creditors seventeen and six in the pound!'

'I daresay,' replied the Old Man, drily.

That kind of thing was wasted on Isaac Henderson.

'Do you want the shop or not? It's just so you and Marthaann have somewhere to live!'

'I've got her somewhere to live!'

'Where?'

'A little flat. In Fifth Avenue.'

'Little? Will it do for the kids?'

'There's only one as far as I know.'

'You'd better look after her, Percy, because if you don't you'll have me to answer to.'

'Isaac,' said the Old Man, 'I don't need any advice from any man, not even you, on how to look after my wife and family.'

Whatever else you might say about the Old Man, he had more front than Buckingham Palace.

So Marthaan and the Old Man and his brother Frank all moved into the small flat where, after Peggy, a boy, Edward, was born. Commons were short, but with Isaac's assistance they managed. The Old Man cannot have been happy but seemed in retrospect to have been more content than he ever was, before or later. Marthaann, young and high-spirited and full of physical energy, missed the large house and the plentiful supply of everything (Isaac bought his oranges and his tea by the barrel), but his Sunday Dinners were lavish as well as compulsory. No drink was taken at these gargantuan spreads, but by now Isaac was drinking secretly and (according to the Old Man) had begun to keep a young woman in a house in Westgate Road, a rather good part of the City.

News of this was not slow in reaching Isaac's wife, Mary, a most formidable lady, who promptly went on an extended holiday to see her young sons in Canada and never returned, divorcing Isaac and later becoming a Doctor, in her fifties. Not bad for the daughter (and wife) of a fishmonger.

Isaac was devastated by this (as he saw it) desertion.

Only one of his seven children was still with him. The rest were living in Canada with their Mother. To Marthaann went all his hopes and affection; but she was married to Percy, who would not come into the Fish Business, so who was he running the Business for?

He began to drink his shops away, one by one.

What the drink didn't do, the War did.

The Kept Woman on Westgate Road had long gone when Isaac reported to the Shipyard for a job as a Master Boiler-maker, his old trade. It was a patriotic decision, according to him. But the Old Man had a theory that the hard work saved him. 'There was a limit to the drinking he could do, hanging on to the side of a ship.'

His shops remained closed all the War.

While the sun no longer shone on Isaac, the Old Man's star was in the ascendant.

He joined the Officer Training Corps of the University of Durham (despite never having attended that establishment) arriving with a Letter of Recommendation from the Officer Commanding Northern Home Forces (a friend of his Father, Edward Prior). He obtained a Commission in the Northum-berland Fusiliers and shipped to France in the March of 1917. He went into the Line not knowing then (or ever) that in the

Trenches opposite served a certain Adolf Hitler of the Second Bavarian List Regiment, a Corporal Meldegänger, or Battalion Runner.

The Fusiliers attacked the Bavarians that same night, the Old Man having been greeted by his Company Commander of nineteen years, a Captain Forman, with the words, 'Glad you're here, old boy, we're going to make a hero of you tonight!'

The Old Man's Company lost more than half its strength and took not an inch of ground. The Old Man refused his Batman's advice to jump into a waterlogged shell-hole until the attack was over.

The Old Man was in the Trenches on and off until the End, finishing with a couple of 'Mentions' but no Military Cross. One was offered to him provided he would take his Company (promotion was fast in the Infantry) on a 'mock' attack. He refused, saying, no doubt mildly, 'I'm not putting my Geordies at risk for a fokkin piece of tin, thank *you*, Sir!'

He was invalided home for the last time in early 1918, suffering from 'Trench Feet', about which nobody knew anything. It was extremely painful and necessitated regular swallows of raw aspirin and whisky combined, to ward off the pain. He left the Battalion Headquarters and trotted down the communications trench to an Ambulance full of dead and dying (driven, to his astonishment, by a young girl VAD), and got in, being conveyed by her to No. 2 instead of No. 1 Casualty Clearing Station.

Later, hobbling on a stick along Piccadilly, an Australian Officer shouted across the traffic, 'Five minutes after you left, Percy, everybody in Battalion HQ copped it! Colonel, Adjutant, Doctor, Everybody!' And disappeared into the crowd.

The Old Man already knew that the Germans had shelled No. 1 Casualty Clearing Station (the one he was supposed to go to) the night he was supposed to *be* there.

All his friends were dead by now, anyway.

Even Captain Forman, whose name he never spoke without a moisture in his eye, had finally gone, disappearing in the Flanders mud in the last days of the War, his fabulous luck giving out at last.

A photograph always hung on the wall of any house the Old Man occupied. It hangs on my wall as I write. It is of twelve young officers who constituted a Hockey team at the Infantry Officer's School at Balliol College, Oxford. The Old Man amongst them. All but two were killed.

I never knew, or I have forgotten, which one was the other man who lived.

After that, the Old Man declared, every day was a bonus.

Like all soldiers after all Wars, he was profoundly unready for the Peace.

He stayed on briefly in the Army, which he loved. 'Felt absolutely at home there. Funny thing that, with all the danger, but there it is . . . Money was the trouble, of course. A Second Lieutenant, to which I'd have had to revert if I stayed on any longer, was paid eleven shillings a day. I'd been getting a Captain's pay and Allowances for the family, so it was no contest: I got out.'

Out was a bigger problem for him than for most.

The Old Man reported to the Officers' Employment Bureau and filled in a form – not, I imagine, without the use of some imagination – and was called for an Interview with a large Brewery Company, with a view to filling a post as a 'Representative'.

The Officers' Employment Bureau wished to give him a

Medical first, just to see (in view of his small Pension) if he was fit to take on this job.

Nobody in the wide world would have thought there was anything sinister in that request.

Nobody except the Old Man.

At the Bureau he was speedily examined and passed on to the Captain-adjutant of the Unit, to whose oily charm he took an instant dislike. 'Typical Home Service wallah. Never seen a Jerry, I'll wager. Handed me a lot of malarkey about what a good job it was, and how I was sure to get it.'

'Did you?'

'Well, first I opened this letter he sent with me, with a red seal, all that, and I read it. As I thought, it was saying I was a perfectly good chap for the job, but my Medical History was against me. The feet, d'yer see?'

'Weren't they against you?'

'Not for that job. It was just a case of going round, taking orders from pub landlords for the amount of beer they wanted next month. You were on trams, trains and buses. It was a gentleman's job and it paid sixty pounds a month, all told.'

'You got it, then?'

'After I tore up that letter I got it.'

'Did nobody ever ask about the letter?'

'How could they? That Captain had the job fixed, for a pal. I knew that.'

It was the Old Man's uncanny ability to read Other People's view of a situation that should have made him a success at anything he undertook. It was based solely on his view that everybody acted, in all situations, out of nothing but sheer self-interest. He didn't blame anybody for that. He didn't care what they did.

He simply *knew* what their interests were, somehow.

It was to all extents and purposes a talent, and was never to leave him. Sometimes, even now, when faced with a problem, I ask myself: what would the Old Man do, if he was here?

It usually helps.

If it does, it is always something I'd never have thought of unaided. But then, I am not the Old Man's Son, but Marthaann's.

Of course, I didn't know that for a very long time.

One never does. I had her genes, as they say nowadays.

While the Old Man was going around the public houses of the North East, pouring unwanted pints of ale into aspidistra-pots (landlords always pulled Reps a drink as soon as they walked in), Marthaann was making ends meet as best she could. It was hand to mouth, for her. The Old Man was in the best job, as a job, he was ever to have; but the truth was he didn't want any job that restrained his movements and his freedom to go to the races or to play billiards for money in the afternoons. Also, fatally, he collected monies from the pub landlords, to pay their accounts at the Brewery. There could only be one end to that.

The Old Man got the Brewery's money ever-so-slightly mixed up with his own. And that was that. Plus, he was always away Racing, and never gave, as they say, proper attention to business.

Dramatic as the loss of the Brewery job was – and to the Old Man it probably wasn't very dramatic, he hated working *for* people – another event overshadowed it.

Isaac Henderson fell under a train.

He had probably drink-taken, but witnesses said that when he jumped on the moving Electric Train at North Shields Station, fresh from the Fish Quay, he did it like a man of twenty. But his flying jacket-pocket caught in the door-handle of the next compartment and the cloth (heavy Yorkshire woollen-suiting, for the rough work amongst the fish) wouldn't tear, and he went down between platform and train.

The view of the Fishing Fraternity was typical.

'It would take a train to kill Isaac Henderson.'

He was sixty.

They gave him the biggest funeral Heaton had ever seen. The end of the procession (the men walked, the women rode in coaches) was still at the door when the hearse reached the Cemetery, half a mile away.

It was a Friday they buried him.

'What will happen to his shops, Martha?' they asked.

Marthaann, tired of bills that were never paid and a husband who was rarely home, did not need long to show she was Isaac's daughter.

'They'll be open on Monday, all four of them,' she said. She closed the flat and moved into Isaac's rambling old house in Heaton (her old home) with her three children (I was two), and put us all in the care of Old Jane, Isaac's housekeeper, a saintly old Cullercoats fisher-lass, who'd worked with the family since she was fourteen.

Marthaann did not consult the Old Man.

She couldn't. He was away racing with his brother Edwards at Ayr in Scotland.

He had sent a Telegram Money Order for ten pounds, his favourite missive for all occasions.

It is said that Marthaann tore it up.

But I bet she didn't.

The Old Man travelled all that summer with Edwards, who was Making a Book at the Race Meetings, and whom the Old

Man had seen only once during the War, when he delivered a batch of Black and Tans to Dublin. He did not serve with them, he simply delivered them, then went, in his officer's uniform, looking for Edwards at an address in Ballsbridge. He didn't know what a risk he was taking, walking around Dublin alone, in uniform.

Edwards opened the door himself. He had spent the entire War in Ireland, where there had been Racing (at Leopardstown and elsewhere) most of the time. On the Mainland, all racing had been cancelled. Edwards was forty by now but taking no chances on the draft. He was to stand, however, on the roof of the Gresham Hotel in Dublin and watch the attack on the Post Office.

A man in a strange uniform, with a feather in his Australian-type Bush Hat, had appeared on the roof with a chit demanding fifty blankets from the astonished Manager, who was standing on the roof with Edwards.

'Fifty blankets?' said the Manager. 'I wouldn't give fifty blankets to Jesus Christ himself.'

'If ye don't ye be meeting Him sooner than ye think,' said the man in the Bush Hat. 'That chit is signed by Connolly.'

'Who the hell's Connolly when he's at home?'

'He's the Commandant of the Irish Republican Army and I'm one of his officers. Do I shoot you now or not?'

'Take the fokkin blankets and bad cess to ye,' retorted the Manager. 'Ye crazy fokkin get!'

When Edwards told that story he always smiled.

Obviously he was no coward.

He just hadn't seen any point in that War.

When the Flat Season was over the Old Man travelled back to Newcastle. It had been a long time, almost all the Summer, and he was looking forward to a break before he joined Edwards for the 'Jumps'. He was a 'Runner', a Floor Man. All he did was to report to Edwards, who stood on his stool at the end of the line (he had good pitches on most tracks; nobody quite knew how or why), any fluctuation in price along the line of Bookmakers. It was important a Bookie didn't get caught out, laying an animal Above the Odds.

It was a job, also, that allowed a man to get a bet on himself, if he felt like it. Unlike the Clerk's job, now filled by his brother Frank, where a man stood with the Book in his hand, working at a speed that, unless you saw it, you would not believe!

But Marthaann had an ultimatum, delivered on the last day. Stay and look after one of the shops. She was down to two, and times were hard, but she was learning. It was an opportunity for them both, surely even he could see that? But the gambling had to stop. And the Racing had to stop.

The Old Man made no reply, but simply picked up his hat.

He never lived with Marthaann again.

'Shall We Make It a Century?'

Edwards won the toss, elected to strike off, and played a safety shot. That is to say, he tried to play a safety shot. He struck the White ball into the pack a little too thickly and instead of coming back smartly down off the top cushion to rest at the other end of the table, in 'baulk' behind the protective row of Yellow, Green and Brown balls, it ran out of legs in the middle of the table and came to a halt, leaving his opponent the choice of two Reds to pot.

This disastrous first shot of the Five-frame match decided the Old Man.

He was out of his chair and moving innocently towards the Gents before the next shot was played. On his way he placed a bet against his brother to win the match. 'His eyes have gone,' the Old Man said, irritably, under his breath, as if Edwards was guilty of some heinous crime. 'He has no right playing for a big-money purse when his eyes are gone.'

The Old Man's bet was a pound at even money, the Butcher to win.

The Butcher was not slow to capitalise on Edwards' mistake.

He made a forty-two break, and went safe.

Edwards failed to score or go safe.

The Butcher took only two more visits to the table to clinch the Frame. His associates and backers, who had several hundred pounds wagered on him around the packed Billiard Room, silent until now, growled their mutual appreciation and doubled their bets.

Edwards polished his glasses and stooped towards me, his dark, expensive waistcoat shiny, and his sleeves and cuffs glistening white. 'Get me a B and S from the bar, will you?'

I started to protest but he had moved away, back into the dark shadows around the bright pool of light over the table. I had been smuggled into the Public Bar by the Old Man. I had no right to be there. I was three years under age. I stared round for the Old Man and saw him talking to a group of the Butcher's friends at the far end of the table. I put my handkerchief on my ringside seat and stole around the back of the crowd, most of whom were standing, holding drinks, and finally corralled the Old Man.

'He wants a B and S,' I said.

'Well, get him one.'

'I can't. You know I'm under age.'

The Old Man looked irritated. 'Oh. All right.'

He returned from the bar with three drinks. The brandy and soda, a whisky and water for himself, and a shandy for me. I didn't want a shandy.

'Drink it up, do you good.'

'I hate the stuff.'

'Leave it then. Better take his drink to Edwards.'

I took the B and S. 'Is the Butcher going to beat him?'

The Old Man sighed. 'The Butcher will pot him off the table.'

'Who have you backed?' I asked, accusingly.

'I have a small interest, that's all.'

Coded, that read: I'm not telling you. But I knew anyway.

Aggrieved, I made my way back to Edwards and handed him the B and S. He sipped it, mildly. He did not seem conscious of the effect his losing the first frame had had on his supporters, who were hastily covering their bets all round the table.

That is to say, those people who had backed Edwards to win, on the strength of his golden reputation, were now backing the Butcher, at much reduced odds, in an effort to cut their losses. In short, they now didn't give him a chance.

I said, 'Can you beat him?'

Edwards did not seem to find the question presumptuous, rather it seemed to him amusing. He glanced at his opponent, the first time I had seen him look. The Butcher was a thickset, bald-headed, perspiring man in his forties.

'The fellow is only a potter,' Edwards said.

I retailed this statement to the Old Man, when he returned and sat on the bentwood chair next to me, sipping his whisky and water.

'The whole object in Snooker is to pot the balls,' said the Old Man.

'I thought safety came into it?'

Edwards was thought to be a master of safety play.

'In the end,' whispered the Old Man, 'nobody ever won a match of five frames playing safety.'

The Butcher struck off for the Second Frame.

It was a perfectly acceptable shot but a pottable Red peeped out of the pack. Most players, especially those the first frame down, would have a try at it, simply to reassure themselves they were in the game. Edwards stared at the Red, bent down as if to attempt to pot it.

'Edwards,' said the Old Man, 'has no more intention of trying to pot that ball than I have.'

It was indeed so. Edwards, blinking mildly, rolled the White ball to safety on the bottom cushion. He seemed oblivious to the mutinous murmur from the spectators, who had come to see a potting match full of fire and the sharp sound of the balls ricocheting into the pockets.

The frame proceeded at a snail's pace.

The Butcher tried hard to set up a break for himself, but it somehow never happened. Just the same, he accumulated points by potting some balls, whereas Edwards seemed content with trying to slow him down.

Nobody in the room could see the point of that.

An elderly man with a silk handkerchief in his top pocket leaned over to me and said, 'The old fellow is playing a waiting game.'

'When he's lost this frame, he'll have waited too long,' said the Old Man, leaning back in his chair and placing a bet against Edwards with a man in the row behind. It was for a pound. I only hoped the Old Man had it.

Edwards lost the Second Frame but not by as large a margin as the first. The Butcher ran out with a thirty-two break, to bursts of muted applause. Almost no bets were struck during the interval before the Third Frame, which was long, as people now went to the bar for fresh drinks.

Edwards chalked his cue with what seemed like quiet melancholy. The Butcher chatted to his backers. The Old Man sprang to his feet, possibly to avoid the eye of Edwards, and seemed to me to place yet another bet at the far end of the table. His seat was unoccupied now, but not for long.

Onkel Frank slid into it. 'What is the position here?'

No salutation. No pleasantries. There never was.

The burning black eyes under the trilby, which seemed to be nailed to his head, bored into mine.

'Edwards has lost two frames.'

'How?'

'Well, he's been playing safety and I suppose it hasn't worked.'

'He would be. And it wouldn't.'

Onkel Frank was a splendid player himself. All three brothers were, except that the Old Man was not in their class. Indeed, the Old Man thought Onkel Frank to be a better player than Edwards. He was, to watch. But as Edwards himself said, 'Frank is a better player than I am but I don't know how it is, I always seem to beat him.'

Onkel Frank played almost no safety shots. Like the Butcher, he was a potter.

Only very rarely are players equally good at both skills, safety and potting. Even professionals.

And professionals were something else. They were a totally different race altogether. They played for their bread and butter, and had none of the style of the great Amateurs, like Onkel Frank.

In many ways, Edwards was a pro.

Edwards had told me a story. Once, as a twenty-year-old, he had played a man for four consecutive frames, at the Station Hotel, Newcastle. The man, whom he didn't know, had beaten him on the Blue each time. At the end, Edwards gave him the four sovereigns and the man had thanked him, adding, 'I'll be back with the four pounds tomorrow night.'

'You don't owe me anything,' Edwards protested. 'It was all fair and square!'

'Yes, but I knew I was going to beat you before we began playing.'

'Not many people can say that,' Edwards had protested.

'I can. My name is Mearton. I am the Professional Snooker and Billiard Champion of Ireland. I know everybody in the world who can beat me at this game and you are not one of them.'

'Why did he need the money?' I had asked.

'Some trouble with a woman, I s'pose, and he'd had to leave Ireland in a hurry.'

The fact that I was only fourteen did not stop the Brothers talking to me in this frank fashion. They all did it, and I was used to it by now.

But Onkel Frank's voice was in my ear, a loud whisper. Onkel Frank was somewhat deaf, but like most deaf people he did not like you to shout.

'Has Edwards said anything about what to bet?'

I shook my head. 'No.'

'Then go and ask him!'

'Now?'

'*What*?'

'Oh. All right.'

Feeling that the eyes of everybody in the room were on me, I stumbled forward, in my school blazer, into the bright lights and then, gratefully, into the shadows, where I found Edwards sitting in a chair, sipping his B and S, and puffing on a Player's Perfecto, the most expensive Virginian cigarette on sale at the time.

'Do you want another drink?' I asked him.

'Why, do you think I need one?'

'No . . . But . . . well . . . Er . . . Onkel Frank's asking . . .'

'Is he? Yes, what?'

'Well, can you recommend a bet?'

'He asked that, did he?'

'Yes.'

'But will he have it if I tell him?' The cool, amused grey eyes bothered me.

'I don't know.'

'I'll have a bet with you he won't.'

'Well, I can only tell him.'

Edwards thought a long moment.

'Tell him he can back me by the frame. From this frame on. If he wants to.'

I nodded, swallowed, and scuttled back to my seat. I hastily recounted this to Onkel Frank.

Onkel Frank was a sometime handicapper, thought by many to be the finest handicapper of dogs in the country, at that time. He did not believe that a dog's performance, that is, its speed, varied at all, unless it was ill or had been given a drink of water before a race. To prove it, he had once handicapped five dogs of exactly equal speed over a given distance and put each one in turn in a red coat – that is, on the inside track and having, therefore, the shortest distance to run. For five meetings running he had run the dogs, putting a different one on the inside track each time. Each time, the dog in the red jacket won.

'The Bookies closed their bags and wouldn't take a bet after the third time,' he reported, testily. 'So much for all this talk about greyhounds running better on heavy or light going, as horses do. That is bullshit and demonstrably not so!'

Onkel Frank's utterances about Racing were somewhat in the manner of Adolf Hitler's about politics. He had a close and lifelong relationship with Adolf Hitler that Adolf Hitler knew nothing about.

After all, he had read all of Darwin, Nietzsche and Schopenhauer (and got me reading them too) just the same as Hitler had, so why wouldn't he feel an affinity? He looked upon Hitler as if he was a bent but redoubtable jockey. 'The man,' he would often say, 'will not be denied.'

The Tory politicians of the day, apart from Churchill, he reviled. Parroting his opinions had got me into trouble at School and I had stopped doing it.

Now he sat, brooding, chewing on the information that I had given him.

At last he pronounced. 'Best of five frames? It's too late.'

'He's only saying a frame at a time.'

'Even so.'

The Billiard Marker (known nowadays as a Referee) was calling the Players to the table.

'Gentlemen! If you please!'

'Aren't you having a bet on him?'

Onkel Frank thought deeply. 'No.'

I found the ten-shilling note in my wallet. Nobody knew I had it. It had come in a letter from Marthaann that morning. I thrust it at Onkel Frank. 'Put this on him for me.'

Onkel Frank looked surprised. 'I thought you didn't bet?'

'I don't, usually.'

He pondered. 'I wouldn't. You'll spew it.'

'Put it on,' I said. 'Any odds you can get!'

Onkel Frank pursed his lips, sighed at greed and innocence, as he saw it. But I knew he had to obey the Racing Man's code. Never put another punter off anything. Ever. If you do, the animal is inclined to win.

Onkel Frank leaned back and breathed a few words to the man behind him. He turned back to me, the ten-shilling note still in his fingers. 'I got you Three-to-One.'

Edwards struck off at that moment.

This time the White ball came sweetly back down the table and rested neatly behind the Brown, snookering the Butcher, who failed to hit anything.

Edwards stepped in purposefully, made twenty-five, and went safe. Twice more he scored and the Butcher didn't. Edwards was now forty points ahead.

The Butcher struck again, scattering the remaining Red balls, a mite desperately, but it was correct play, as it challenged Edwards to a potting match, which the Butcher felt he must win.

Edwards made a chanceless thirty-six break and ran out the winner of the Frame. But he was still Two-One down.

Onkel Frank collected the thirty shillings from the man in the row behind and offered it to me. I said, 'Put the two pounds on Edwards for the next Frame, if he wants it.'

The man did, but at Two-to-One now. I was on four pounds plus my own two, when Edwards won the Fourth Frame, which he did easily, as the Butcher's potting talent seemed to suddenly desert him.

I had even noticed Edwards commiserating with his opponent, in a friendly way. The Butcher had merely nodded and gone on to miss a Black that nine times out of ten he wouldn't have missed.

The man in the row behind refused a bet on the last Frame, which Edwards won, playing some safety but a lot more attacking shots. His was an easy victory and he shook hands with two fingers with his opponent, in the Edwardian fashion.

The elderly man with the silk handkerchief said to me, 'The old fellow out-generalled him.'

The Butcher gave Edwards ten large white flimsies.

Edwards put them in his waistcoat pocket in a smooth and

practised movement, and I gave him another B and S. He looked at it in surprise. 'Thank 'ee.' He mused, 'Did Frank have a bet?'

'I don't think so,' I said, carefully.

'Ah,' said Edwards. He was smiling his easy smile.

'I did,' I said.

'I thought you didn't bet.'

'Well, I don't. Not usually.'

'Why this time?'

I couldn't tell him the truth. 'You don't lose many matches, do you?'

'Nearly did, this one.'

'No!'

'Oh, but yes. Know how I won it?'

'You scored more points.'

'That's only part of it. We were playing for fifty pounds. After the Second Frame, when I'd lost two Frames, I asked the Butcher if he wanted to make it a Century. On the match.'

'Wasn't that unwise?'

'No. He couldn't refuse. But a hundred pounds is a lot of money to him.'

'Not to you?'

'No, not to me.' He sighed. 'What did Percy do?'

'No idea.'

He nodded disbelievingly and put his cue in the tin case. A minute later, avoiding the congratulations of his supporters, he was out of the Billiard-room.

The Old Man was at my elbow. 'I hear you backed Edwards?'

'I did. Won six pounds.'

'Yes?' the Old Man said. 'I'm in a bit of a hole myself. I was sure the Butcher would beat him.'

'How much?'
'A fiver would do it.'
I gave him the fiver.
After all, I didn't approve of betting.

'When Is a Rabbit Pie?'

The Old Man was in the Final of the Christmas Snooker Handicap.

It was nothing new.

He got to the Finals or the Semis of some club or pub every year because he was that rarity, a player who kept his bottle, indeed improved on his game the more there was at stake. He revelled in every kind of money match, particularly when he couldn't pay if he lost. And, along with everybody else, I was almost tired of seeing him extricate himself from impossible situations to win. He almost always needed to pot all the colours to take a vital frame, and almost always he did just that.

Often against players far better than he was.

Sometimes, he was shaping up to pot the next colour before the previous ball was safely in the pocket, but still rolling gently across the green baize towards it.

'Nay, Percy,' his opponents would cry in anguish, 'wait for the bloody ball to drop!'

But the Old Man had played the next ball by then.

This year he was not only in the final at the Working Men's Club, he was also in a dilemma.

The First Prize was a Goose.

The Second Prize was Four Bags of Coal.

And the Final was to be played very late on Christmas Eve, far too late to buy a chicken or a duck or some replacement for the Goose if he lost. Yet if he bought a bird of any kind now (it was six o'clock on Christmas Eve) it would, in his own words, be 'Supernumerary to Strength'.

'Which means what?' I asked.

'It's an Army phrase and it means "too much".'

'I don't see what choice you have,' I said. 'If you lose, we can't eat four bags of coal for our Christmas dinner.'

The Old Man never cared for these kind of realities being pointed out to him. 'I'll have something for Jane to cook, and it'll be that fokkin Goose!'

'Who are you playing?'

'Hooky Walker and he's giving me three blacks, best of three frames.'

I was not reassured. Hooky Walker was a local man, the proprietor of not one but two Amusement Stalls on the Pleasure Beach and an extremely steady snooker player. What they called, in those days, a bread-and-butter player. He was also 'not without', that is to say, had money, and was not likely, in the Old Man's phrase, to take in water under pressure.

I said as much.

The Old Man looked irritated. 'He's giving me twenty-one points in each frame. He can't do it.'

'You're well handicapped?' I enquired.

'I never go in that club, and they hardly know me. The few times I've been in I've played badly.'

That, I realised, was no accident. The club Handicapper

had obviously thought he couldn't play and had handicapped him too favourably in consequence.

I went to get my bike out of the shed. Jane, the House-keeper, appeared at my elbow. She had been cooking and baking all day and her arms, up to the elbows, were covered in flour.

'What's your Father doing about the Christmas Dinner?' she whispered. She had disapproved of the Old Man from the first day she had seen him. She blamed him for every-thing, starting with getting Marthaann pregnant twenty-odd years before. The fact that she now lived under his roof and not Marthaann's made no difference. She often managed to get through an entire day without speaking to him. He did not seem to notice.

Naturally, she received no wages for her work.

But then, she never had.

'He'll win the Goose,' I said, as confidently as I could. I felt sorry for Jane. After all, she had brought me up. She had brought Marthaann and her brothers and sisters up, too. We all owed her a lot.

'If we're relying on that,' said Jane, wiping her floury hands on her long, white apron, 'we might be eating bread and cheese for our Christmas Dinner.'

'Never!' I said stoutly.

'Where are you off to?'

'Jack's.'

Jack was my friend. His father was a Baker.

'He's a nice-enough young lad,' said Jane, 'Jack.'

What she meant was that Jack was not gentry or anything like it. Even the Old Man, with all his faults, was a Gent. Mr Ashworth, the Baker, covered in a fine coat of white flour every day but Sunday, was a working man; self-employed, granted, but a Working Man all the same. Jane, a servant all her life, was a snob about these sort of things. That did not alter the fact that, had Mr Ashworth asked her, she would, as they used to say, have given him the coat off her back.

She felt, much more keenly than I did, the fact that I no longer went to a posh School. I hadn't cared for the Prep School. I had got into trouble for playing football with the Raggy-lads, the barefoot slum-boys of Byker. I found Jack a good friend and we shared the same pleasures: sport and books.

Jack had read, according to his father Harold, whom he called Stiffy, every book in the Blackpool Public Library. He was also the best young batsman I'd ever seen, and even by then I'd seen a lot of cricketers. Mr Ashworth had played for Nelson in the Lancashire League, but he had given up on Jack, who treated every ball bowled at him as something to hit. Mr Ashworth was in despair at such a carefree attitude to a serious business.

'A felly as con break 'em both ways will geet thee out every time,' he told his son.

'Not,' said Jack, 'if they don't bounce.'

Mr Ashworth would hear no good words about his son's cricketing ability, however carefully and politely offered.

'He's nobbut a big felly,' he would say.

A big felly is a lad who thinks he's a man.

It wasn't true of Jack. He simply had a great eye. And great feet. I knew that all too well. I had won the Silver Cup for the bowling averages and I simply couldn't get Jack out.

'You're too accurate,' he told me. 'Try bowling me a bad 'un now and then.'

I couldn't do that, and so I stood and watched my best off-spin disappearing over the sight-screen.

Everybody said he would play for Lancashire. Or anyway in the Lancashire League, for one of the big clubs, Nelson or Colne or Rawtenstall.

He joined the RAF in the War, aged eighteen, was badly wounded and played for nobody. But none of us knew that then.

Jack was in when I got to his house, sitting in front of the fire, reading. It was a novel by a writer called Evelyn Waugh, of whom I knew nothing and who I supposed to be a woman. 'It's good,' said Jack, 'woman or not.'

I didn't argue with him. He'd already found Auden, Isherwood and MacNeice. He had a knack for it. At school he was not thought to be scholastic or talented in any way. He was totally without ambition and, as they say nowadays, went with the flow. He was not tall but very strong and brave and modest.

Everybody liked him.

Jack got on extremely well with the Old Man and would often make surreptitious bets with his pocket-money, through the agency of the Old Man. I thought he was stupid and said so, but he just laughed. He laughed at most things, especially his father, but affectionately.

Now, there was a crisis.

Mr Ashworth had not been home for his supper, that was the problem. Mrs Ashworth, known to all as Sannah, an open-hearted and saintly woman of the kind you rarely see nowadays, sat on a sofa smoking a Woodbine, her only vice. She had not had an easy life, having nursed Mr Ashworth through the trauma of his experiences in the War, when he had been blown up and buried by a shell-burst.

He had been driving an ammunition lorry at the time.

Fortunately, it had not blown up.

As Sannah recounted the story, it had taken two hours to dig him out. 'He's not been the same since, hasn't Harold,' she said. 'You have to make allowances, you know, Allan.'

Mr Ashworth, for his part, lived his life as if the War had not happened. On coming back to Nelson, the small Lancashire cotton town where he lived, after demobilisation, he had found that his 'natural-brother' Tommy (born, as they used to say, on the wrong side of the blanket) disputed his right to the small bakery, left by their joint-father, who had died while they were fighting in France.

To settle the matter they had fought a fist-fight along the towpath of the canal, next to the disputed bakery. Mr Ashworth had finally knocked his half-brother into the water. 'Tommy saw sense then,' reported Mr Ashworth. 'He knew right from wrong. He knew the bakery was rightly mine, not his.' Mr Ashworth would sip his boiling-hot tea. 'He were a good lad, were Tommy. We allus have a drink together if we meet anywheer, in a pub or owt.'

Such delicate things were settled simply in those days.

Now, Sannah was troubled.

'I know your father never lets me down,' she said to Jack, who had returned to reading Evelyn Waugh, probably the only person in Blackpool, that or any other day, who was.

'But he hasn't been home at all, and I don't know what we're having for our Christmas Dinner tomorrow, I do not.'

Something stopped me from saying Snap.

Jack closed Evelyn Waugh and stood up and put on his coat. 'We'll go along to the Bakery and see what he's got.'

Sannah brightened and lit another Woodbine. 'He's never let me down yet, hasn't Harold,' she repeated.

As we walked to the Bakery, all of two miles, I debated telling Jack about the Old Man's problem with the Goose, but decided not to. I was under invitation to have my Christmas Dinner at Jack's house, after the Blackpool versus Manchester City Football Match on the Christmas Morning. I hadn't told anybody about that. Jane would not be pleased. But my sister Peggy and her Fiancé would be there, as would my brother Ted and Onkel Frank and the Old Man, so I wouldn't be missed. I decided to ask Jack to come and have Christmas Dinner with us, if the Old Man won the Goose, or if Mr Ashworth finally let his Wife down.

It seemed a lot of ifs.

We found Mr Ashworth in the Bakehouse.

He was dressed, as ever, in a cap, a collarless shirt, and two waistcoats. He had nothing on his feet save his socks. 'It's too hot for boots in this place,' he had explained to me.

The Bakehouse was a large, low shed, a timber frame, covered by sheets of wavy black corrugated-iron. It housed a huge coke-oven, which never went out, providing Mr Ashworth with an excuse to stay away from home at any hour he liked, since when he was asked where he was going he had merely to snarl, 'I'm goin' t'Fire, wheer else would I be goin'?'

His destination, mostly, was the Working Men's Club, a hundred yards away from the Bakehouse, where he could get a drink at any hour of the day and much of the night. He would run from the Bakehouse to the back door of the Club in his stocking-feet, through snow or rain, replying when asked why, 'Nay, they'll dry off in theer in two-thri minutes.'

Mr Ashworth always seemed to run. Now, he was charging at his oven with a delicate pattern of biscuit-dough arranged on his large, shovel-like platter.

'Why is your father always in such a hurry?' I asked Jack.

'Because he has to get a drink and he has to get a bet on.'

Now, Mr Ashworth clanged his oven door shut, and turned, a ghostly whitened figure (he was covered in a thin film of flour), and asked, 'What do you two want?'

He was not a man who'd win prizes for charm.

But we were only felly-lads after all, and hardly worth conversing with. It was the usual attitude to youth in those days, and we did not resent it.

'You've not been home to your tea,' said Jack.

'Fire needed doin'.' Mr Ashworth rubbed his whiskers (he only shaved on Sundays) and a fine cloud of flour erupted from them. It was as well that his customers, the Boarding-house landladies, did not see him as he was now, or the Bakehouse itself, for that matter. It was infested with cock-roaches and every other known insect, and would today be condemned on sight. 'But,' asked Jack, 'where would you go to get a better biscuit?'

He was right. Ginger, Cinnamon, Treacle, Shortcake, they melted in the mouth. Mr Ashworth's band of door-to-door salesmen, each and every one of them in some way handi-capped, rarely lost a customer once they'd got her. Led by Joel, a severely-gassed and irritable old War veteran, who lived in a caravan on the marshy site where the Bakery stood, they attacked the Landladies of Blackpool Monday to Friday.

'Theer's not many as'll refuse a cripple,' Mr Ashworth would say thoughtfully, sipping his rum and hot water. 'They're money in the bank, are fellas wi' one leg.'

Almost all this strange band, carrying large baskets filled with biscuits covered by pristine white napery, were War veterans in receipt of a pension. The biscuit-selling was a moonlighting job. Nobody, in those hard times, seemed to find anything odd or wrong about it.

Jack returned to the attack, dropping into the dialect. 'Nah then, Stiffy, hasta geeten owt for t'Christmas Dinner?'

'Nay,' said Mr Ashworth, pensively making a Baker's mark with his thumbnail on a spare piece of dough. Every Baker, in those days, had his own mark. Mr Ashworth, according to Jack, didn't know why he did it, and was oblivious to the fact that Bakers had been doing it since the Middle Ages. It had been taught to him as an Apprentice, so he just did it.

'Not a turkey or a goose?' Jack persisted.

'Nay,' said his father. It was impossible to tell if he was protesting or simply denying the question.

'Not a duck or a chicken, or owt like that?' asked Jack.

Mr Ashworth was tiring of this. 'Nay!' he said for the last time, spun on his heel and with sudden alacrity was out of the Bakehouse, still in his stocking-feet, and across the damp, not to say wet, ground, and in the back door of the Working Men's Club.

Jack pursued him to the door but found his way barred by the Custodian, a large man in a dark linen overall. 'Now, you two lads know you can't come in 'ere,' he said. 'You're under age by a while yet.'

'Nay, bloody hell,' said Jack.

'No need for language,' said the Custodian.

'What time does the Club loose?' asked Jack.

'Tonight?' The Custodian took out his watch and looked at it. It was large and engraved. 'We've an extension on while midnight. Snooker Final's on.' He acknowledged my existence. 'Your Father's in it, isn't he, lad?'

'Yes,' I said, avoiding Jack's eye.

'I still can't let you in,' said the Custodian.

'No, I know,' I said.

We turned away, defeated. As we walked back towards Jack's house, he said, 'I didn't know Percy was in the Final.'

We called our fathers, in private, by their first names. It was a way of reducing their power over us, but in fact they didn't have much. They were, neither of them, men like most Fathers of the time, who ruled their sons by diktat. It could have been because they didn't care enough, but my theory was that they'd been in that War a long time and it had given them a perspective on what mattered and what didn't. It came under the Old Man's heading: every day's a bonus.

Sannah was strangely unconcerned to hear that her husband had as yet made no provision for the Christmas Dinner. She merely reiterated that Harold had never let her down, and supplied us with sandwiches of brawn, and hot sweet tea, as we played a few hands of German Whist with her. Cards were her passion. She was an excellent player and a patient teacher. I found it interesting and took in her rules. 'Third player always plays high,' and 'Think hard about what your partner leads with. He wants you to come back at him with that suit, you see?'

She was a lovely woman with a lovely name, Susannah, shortened to Sannah, which was almost as good. She came from a better-off family than her husband. Her father, and now her brother, were In Scrap. Put another way, they bought metal and rags from the redoubtable Rag and Bone men. It was – according to her brother Wallace who, well-dressed and driving a car, sometimes called at the house, distributing only moderate largesse – not a profession for faint hearts. Chicanery and cheating were common, violence not unknown.

Still, as Wallace said, there was money in it.

Not that Wallace spread it around. He stuck to what he

had. As Sannah commented mildly, 'Much wants more, you know, Allan.'

It was the nearest she ever got to a criticism of anybody.

Now, she was happy, shuffling and dealing the cards, under the holly and the mistletoe and the tree, all bought for a few coppers from Rutter's the greengrocer on Highfield Road. The baking had been done, the mince-pies and cakes (Mr Ashworth never, ever entered the kitchen at home), and the vegetables peeled and left in water against the morning. Neither Jack nor I expected much in the way of presents. He would probably get a book (thought to be an eccentric choice) from his parents. I was in for a new pair of football boots (I was forever growing out of them) but was not, as they say nowadays, holding my breath where the Old Man was concerned.

To the background of radio music we played cards until ten o'clock, when Jack's sister Mary appeared with her fiancé, Cedric. She was a dark, striking girl of eighteen, who had worked fourteen hours a day for the last week in her Uncle's Cake-shop on Highfield Road, both serving in the shop and working in the small bakery behind it. Cedric was a First Counter-hand at the Co-operative and was thought to have prospects. He came of Methodist family and he was considered a Good Lad. He too had worked very long hours all through Christmas week, probably ten hours on average each day for no extra pay. Nobody then thought it odd or wrong. It was Christmas, that was all.

Everybody had Christmas Day and Boxing Day off, unless it fell on a Sunday, in which case they didn't.

Nobody thought that odd, either.

Except me, because I came from a family where nobody worked for anybody, as such. I marvelled then, as I marvel now, at such acceptance and good temper. The Old Man always called the British Working Man 'The Salt of the Earth', but showed a firm reluctance to join him in his labours.

The entry of Mary and Cedric created a small sensation.

For Cedric had a large Alsatian dog on a chain.

'It's a thoroughbred,' said Cedric, in explanation.

It was a remark worth making, as almost nobody in the town owned a thoroughbred dog. Mongrels of all shapes and sizes were common and their puppies given away free, but a thoroughbred dog was rare and a thoroughbred Alsatian even rarer.

All remarked on the animal.

'It'll eat a fair bit, you know,' said Sannah, 'will that dog. It'll eat you out of house and home, Cedric.'

'Oh, Mother, it'll not,' said Mary.

'Does it bite?' asked Jack.

'It will if you plague it,' said Cedric, equably.

I said nothing. The Alsatian bared its teeth. It seemed to know we were talking about it.

'Where's my Dad?' asked Mary.

'At Bakehouse,' said Sannah, defensively.

'Tending Fire, I suppose?' said Mary, a spirited girl.

'Getting tomorrow's dinner,' answered Sannah, lighting a Woodbine, a sure sign she was troubled.

'You mean we've nothing for our Christmas Dinner yet?' asked Mary, with a scandalised glance towards Cedric. 'Oh, he does show us up, Mother, he really does!'

And with that she went upstairs to wash and change. Cedric sat imperturbably on, smoothing the Alsatian's fur and whispering in its ear. I asked the dog's name.

'Tiger,' said Cedric.

'He's nowt like a tiger,' said Jack.

'You'd think he was,' Cedric said, 'if he got hold of you.'

The dog growled again. Jack and I went upstairs to his bedroom and played some jazz records. We had Bix and Louis Armstrong and Fats Waller. Jack played the records so often that he had all but worn them out. He took a trumpet from its case and played to the records. Played was an exaggeration, as all he did was blow long, blasting metallic notes that shook the windows. He was taking lessons at a half-crown a time from Freddy Jeffries, a bucolic man who played in the pit-orchestra at the Palace Varieties. He must have been Freddy's worst pupil. 'I con hear him on't bowling-green,' reported Mr Ashworth. The bowling-green was a quarter of a mile from the house.

As he played we became conscious of a series of thumps on the partition wall between Jack's wall and the next-door house. Obviously somebody objected to the noise, even on Christmas Eve.

'Who's that?' I asked.

'Old Whalley. He sometimes does it.'

Old Whalley was an elderly but robust crippled man who walked with the aid of two sticks. He had a furious temper at the best of times and had been known to tell tram-conductors they were 'Bloody wooden-heads' when they failed to put him off at the right stop. Nobody crossed him if they could help it.

His hammering went on for some time.

Finally, Jack stopped blowing the trumpet and put it back in the case. We went downstairs.

'Was that old Mister Whalley knocking?' asked Sannah.

Mary was downstairs by now, in her finery. A blue dress and her hair done. She looked very good but she wasn't going anywhere. Nobody did on Christmas Eve. Where was there to go?

She said, 'Jack's showing us up again. He ought to get rid of that trumpet. He'll never learn to play it. He doesn't practise at all. He thinks he can learn by just blowing it.'

What she said was true. Jack liked the idea of being a trumpet player in a big band like Benny Goodman's (or even Nat Gonella's) but he was a born appreciator, not a doer. He hadn't learned that about himself yet, however.

'I'd practise more if Old Whalley didn't knock on that wall every time I start!' he protested.

Said Sannah mildly, 'His wife tells me he hadn't been upstairs for nearly fifteen years until he went up to knock on that wall.'

'Nay, bloody hell,' said Jack, under his breath, and collapsed in a chair.

'Watch that chair and your language,' said Mary, with a sideways glance at Cedric who, as a Methodist, disapproved of language, which he heard all around him all day at the Co-op where, despite the name of the firm, few employees had Socialist Brotherhood attitudes.

'Probably a reaction against having to be nice to the customers all day,' said Jack.

The clock ticked on.

Quarter to twelve.

Ten to twelve.

Cedric and Mary went out for a walk round the block, obviously to kiss, a shaming and daring thing to do but perhaps permissible on Christmas Eve. They took the Alsatian with them.

Five to twelve.

Mr Ashworth arrived on the stroke of midnight.

He stood in the kitchen doorway, swaying slightly. His cap was no longer straight on his head and he had a fixed smile on his face. Two bottles protruded from the pockets of his jacket.

'Nay, Harold,' said Sannah.

'Nay, Sannah,' said Mr Ashworth.

I could stand the suspense no longer.

'Did my father win the Final?' I asked.

Mr Ashworth frowned at me. I was nobbut a lad and hardly worthy of a reply. After a long pause, he said, 'No.'

'No?' I felt shattered. What now?

'I backed him,' said Mr Ashworth. 'I lost money on him.'

'Nay, Harold,' said Sannah, lighting a Woodbine.

Mr Ashworth remained almost motionless in the dark doorway to the kitchen. Almost, because I could see he swayed slightly.

'I backed him and Hooky Walker beat him on the last black.'

I took a deep breath. 'Then all he got was four bags of coal?'

'Aye,' said Mr Ashworth, with genuine regret. 'But he got these an' all!'

Slowly, Mr Ashworth took his hands from behind his back like a conjuror and held up two unskinned rabbits.

At that moment the front door clicked and Cedric and Mary and the Alsatian came into the room.

'Nay, Dad,' said Mary disgustedly, seeing her Father swaying in the kitchen doorway. 'Do right!'

Mr Ashworth held up the rabbits high, for all to see.

'Percy has two as well,' he said. 'He swapped the coal with Joe Hyton, the Market Gardener, for 'em!'

He added, in total admiration, 'Dosta know what Percy

said? He said, "When is a Rabbit Pie?" Dosta see? "*When* is a Rabbit Pie?" '

We all waited.

'When it has a crust round it!'

We just stared.

Mr Ashworth repeated, 'When it has a crust round it!' and shook his head in silent mirth.

At that, the Alsatian, knowing him for a benefactor, leaped up and placed two paws on Mr Ashworth's shoulders and stared long into his face.

'Nay!' said Mr Ashworth, who had not realised the dog was in the room.

The Alsatian dropped to the floor and took one of the rabbits in his mouth, and retreated into a corner, growling.

It took five minutes to get that rabbit from that dog.

But it tasted all right on Christmas Day.

'Top Weight'

Onkel Frank, before he returned to the family fold in Blackpool, had served several stints as a handicapper of greyhounds. He was thought by many to be the best in the
country.

Dogs, until the early Thirties, had meant greyhounds (chasing hares) and whippets (chasing rabbits) at flapping (illegal)
or legal meetings, held in freezing fields by half a hundred
people, often in the North of England. The White City Greyhound Stadium, opened in London in the late Twenties,
changed all that. The Management provided housing, food
and water for the dogs, and owners put their animals in the
kennels in the care of 'Lads', the whole thing looked after by
a Manager (often of military background, to indicate probity)
and a small Staff.

To the astonishment of the Racing Fraternity, punters
flocked to see greyhounds chase an imitation hare, under
floodlights, around a race-track at White City. The Old
Racing Hands could not understand it. Where was the fun?
No long, freezing journey to Towcester or Wincanton or
Cartmel or Ayr – just a tube-train trip to West London. Of
an evening, at that.

Still, the punters went as did their cash. Sometimes in very large amounts.

Small bets, granted. But a hell of a lot of them.

It took thinking about. It did, the Race-track Bookies confessed to each other, raking the last of the silver out of their bags in the damp and dismal Bookies' sheds at Chester or Newcastle; it took thinking about.

One of those who thought about it was Edwards.

Still smarting from his refusal to put money into Football Syndicates ('The Ordinary Man Will Never Bet on Footballers'), he was inclined to take Greyhound Racing more seriously. For one thing, the Tote was running On-Course Bookmaking. Until the Tote, which gave the punters a large proportion of their money back, appeared on British race-tracks, the Bookies had never paid odds above Six to One. Now the Tote was paying out Outsiders at a Hundred to One!

It was, without doubt, said the Bookies, champing on their cigars, ruining the Game.

The old way was done.

The old way, the skilled Bookies like Edwards could Bet Round – that is to say, whatever animal won, the Book won. Bookies like Edwards didn't gamble. They manipulated their prices so that they took exactly as much money on each animal as they wanted to, and not a penny more. It was a great skill, now entirely lost.

Most Bookies nowadays rely on the Mug Punter or Guesser to piss his money away looking for One To Beat The Favourite.

Fortunately there is an endless supply of these punters.

The Old Man being a prime example.

When the Greyhound Track opened at Blackpool, Edwards

was amongst the first to take it seriously enough to apply for a Bookie's Pitch in the Best Ring, and get it.

Somehow, the Depression didn't affect Dog-tracks too much, as a Day Out at a Race-Meeting cost at least a fiver before you had a bet, whereas a Dog-track cost you your fare to the place and a couple of shillings' entrance money.

Greyhounds were plainly the Future.

Especially at a place like Blackpool where, as the saying had it, Yorkshire fellas went to see Lancashire fellas throwing their money about!

Edwards booked in at the best hotel in the area, the Metropole at St Anne's, and got to work. He had Frank, in an off-period as a handicapper, clerking for him.

The crowds were huge.

As Edwards said, 'Two meetings a day, six days a week. I can Bet Round, I can't lose, and I always win fifty pounds a meeting.'

Frank grunted. He was being paid two pounds a meeting.

That was ten pounds a week and beat a provincial Bank Manager by two pounds. Still, Onkel Frank did not think it enough. A Bad Paymaster, Edwards, was his verdict.

'We're doing pretty well here,' said Edwards, one day, treating Onkel Frank to a large whisky in the Palatine Hotel on Blackpool's sea-front.

'Not bad,' grunted Onkel Frank. He was living in digs in South Shore, a Combined Room (that is, bed and a gas-ring), but it suited his needs. He had never married, asking, 'Why should I keep Another Man's Daughter?'

Said Edwards, mildly blinking into his B and S, 'I've been thinking. Should we send for Percy?'

Onkel Frank's reply was prompt and acerbic.

'No. Certainly not.'

Onkel Frank had lived with his brother almost all of his life, excepting the War years. The Old Man was a wearing and unnerving companion on a day-to-day basis, starting with his getting them both arrested by the Police on his fourteenth birthday. The Northumberland Constabulary had raided a Miners' Sunday Pitch-and-Toss School, on the sand-dunes at Newbiggin. They had appeared, Onkel Frank reported, as if by magic, heavy and perspiring men in tight blue uniforms, grabbing as many men as they could hold. They had several Black Marias standing by.

The Inspector was astonished to find two schoolboys amongst the catch. On learning that they were the sons of Mr Edward Prior, and attended the local Boys' Academy, he was nonplussed and took them home personally.

'You need to keep your eye on these two, Sir,' he advised, taking whisky in my Grandfather's study.

An eye was kept. My Grandfather bought the boys a Billiard table to keep them out of trouble, and the rest was history.

After his death, and the money going, the Brothers got a job in Newcastle collecting rents, in the many foul tenements of the city.

Onkel Frank worked out a way of collecting the rents faster, by changing the routes the previous collectors had taken. He was given no extra money for this.

The Old Man drew Frank's wages as well as his own for the first week, and gambled them away before Frank could get to him.

This meant no dinners for a week, or at best a pair of kippers, in their small Combined Room.

And occasioned a fist-fight.

Not the first or the last, as brothers, in those days, defended each other against the world, but found it obligatory to use physical force to put a personal injustice right. With the Old Man, this didn't work. Nothing, reported his brother, was ever going to change him.

Onkel Frank had periodically, to gain breath, loosened his bonds with the Old Man, and Blackpool, no doubt, seemed a refuge. Frank was totally honest and, like most handicappers, rarely bet; and never owed money to anybody.

Therefore, almost always he had some.

A fact not unknown to the Old Man.

Now, sitting in the lounge of the palatial Palatine Hotel in Blackpool, a league away from Newcastle and its slums and obvious poverty, he was startled at Edwards' suggestion.

'Bringing Percy here would only bring a host of trouble with it.' He lit his thirtieth Player's of the day. He was a thinking man, and tobacco was known to be an aid to thinking, then.

'Even so,' said Edwards, 'he writes telling me he's given up his job managing that Billiard hall and is looking for something else to do.'

'Let him find it,' said Onkel Frank, 'elsewhere.'

'I don't know,' said Edwards, on whom the duty of keeping the family together had fallen, with his father's sudden death. 'I think he could get a job here, clerking on the Track.'

'He's no clerk,' said Onkel Frank, who was a brilliant clerk.

'No, I know,' replied Edwards. 'But it doesn't matter for the Dogs. There's only five of them running in each race. It's child's play.'

'Who would teach him,' asked Onkel Frank, 'if he came?'

Edwards lit a havana and blew out clear blue smoke. 'Well, you, I suppose.'

Onkel Frank nodded, resigned. It was more or less what

he expected. The Old Man followed him about, as they used to say then, like a bad penny.

'Don't say I didn't warn you.'

Edwards sent for Percy.

The Old Man moved in with Onkel Frank, much to the latter's annoyance, and promptly obtained (after a week's tuition) a job as a clerk with a man called Ken Virgo, who wore a long camel-hair coat and no hat; odd, for the time. Virgo pulled his prices, laying animals at longer odds than anybody else in the line, including Edwards, whose muted, gentlemanly remark, 'Any Price yer like, some of these Runners, any Price yer like, some of these Dogs,' was lost in the raucous bellowing of his neighbours.

The highest price on his Board, as the Old Man said, being Five to Two.

Edwards, a wild and high liver in many ways, was a respected tight-arse where the Odds were concerned. The old North-country Bookie had taught him well.

The Old Man further offended Onkel Frank by receiving five pounds a week more from Virgo than Frank was getting from his brother. The Old Man seemed finally free of his domestic entanglements, as he had left everybody behind in Newcastle. Marthaann, obviously, and the rest of the family, too.

For a Season he lived a life of freedom. Good money, comfortable lodgings, a new town where few people knew him and consequently his credit was good. Who could ask for more?

It could not last.

The disaster, from the Old Man's point of view, came about in an innocent way. Blackpool was a famous seaside resort: the Tower, the Winter Gardens, the three Piers. It was and is the greatest seaside resort in the world, if you like that sort of thing. The Old Man did not particularly, and like everybody else who lived in the town for any length of time, he was soon able to simply ignore the hordes of visitors, red-faced from the sun, crowding the Prom and the bars, by the simple means of not going where they were. The Prom. The large public bars. The Tower Ballroom. The Open Air Baths. The Sands.

None of the Brothers ever went near any of those places. They went to quiet local pubs and they took trams around the back of the town at the height of the Season, and (if they were the Old Man or Onkel Frank) they kept their hats and their collars and ties on at all times. Edwards didn't even live in the place, but in a Five-star hotel in St Anne's, five miles up the coast.

To other people, my sister Peggy and my brother Ted, and particularly me, still living in Newcastle, the very idea of Blackpool was exciting. We all came, with Jane the house-keeper in charge, for a holiday. We stayed in digs near the Old Man and Onkel Frank, and we swam and played football on the Sands and went on the rides at the Pleasure Beach and did all the things all visitors do. The result was we liked it very much. We thought it was Paradise.

To get that into perspective, you have to remember that Newcastle was an Unemployment Black Spot, with enormous numbers of workless men hanging around every street corner. Men who had fought and won the War, with teeth gone from rotten food at thirty years of age, and hungry children at home, living at about the subsistence level of a Cambodian peasant today. By the luck of having the Shops, and somehow keeping one or two of them open, Marthaann was making enough money to live, comfortably. She was working every hour of the day to do it.

So she was glad to see the rest of her family in Blackpool with their father. Let him have them for a bit. See how he liked it!

The Old Man didn't mind it. For a while.

He had been away Racing or in the Army most of my young life, although I always as a child liked what I saw of him. He had none of the strict Methodism Marthaann inherited from Isaac (and against which her natural good health and high spirits rebelled) and was always handy with a gift of money or a new football, or the School Fees.

Also, he kept money in each and every pocket, and had a habit of giving a coin to every child he met, after first enquiring their name, then passing on to whatever business he had to do. This brief encounter made him immensely popular with all children, including his own, who were included in this pleasant ritual.

Suddenly it must have dawned on him that some of the family were not going home. My brother Ted went, for he was in his last year as an Apprentice Draughtsman at one of the few shipyards still open on the Tyne; and Peggy went back to help out in the Shops, a bit of a come-down after the Newcastle Central School for Girls, but times were hard and getting harder.

Jane it was who corralled the Old Man. She reminded him of his duties.

'Marthaann has more than enough to do, running the Shops and looking after the other two. I think I should stay here with the Boy for the rest of the summer, and then we'll see.'

The Old Man was too busy or too gullible or too uncaring

to think how that would end. It opened up the possibility of Jane and myself staying longer. Even permanently.

Oddly, he didn't seem to mind.

It could have been conscience but I think it more likely it was the fact that I wanted to stay that tickled his vanity. I liked Blackpool. It was a massive improvement on Newcastle from the point of view of a lively boy: plenty of good air, sport and the possibility of a different kind of life.

The fact was, when Jane said I needed a father she was right. I'd grown up with Marthaann, my sister Peggy, and Jane, with my brother Ted there only when he wasn't working or studying. And I found it tiresome. Women, I thought, were all right but they fussed too much and they issued far too many piddling orders. The Old Man promised a larger view of life, a freer view, and I plumped for it. It was as simple as that.

The Old Man found Jane unhappy living in lodgings, which she regarded, naturally, as low behaviour. And so he semi-reluctantly rented a largish house in South Shore and moved us in. First, he filled it with furniture on the HP, what he called the 'Kathleen' after the old Irish song 'Kathleen Mavourneen', one line of which goes: 'It may be for years, Or it may be for ever.'

I couldn't understand this cavalier attitude to life and living, but it came as a nice change after the restrictions of Marthaann's Methodist way of doing things, which involved not much fun and prompt payment of bills.

Not that Marthaann was a killjoy. Far from it.

She just hadn't discovered that about herself yet.

So when Ted was discharged from his job in the Shipyard (because it closed) he came South to Blackpool and a job as a clerk in Edwards' office. The Old Man was able to say, with some justification, 'They all came for the holidays and every last one of them stayed!'

In truth, it was nothing he expected to happen.

Of course there was a shuttle-service of visitors from Black-pool to Newcastle, but none the other way. It worked well enough. Jane ran the house and didn't expect wages. Nobody had paid her wages since Isaac died. She was, sink or swim, one of the family. To us all, she was an emotional link with the old life. Meantime, life went on; the Old Man was making very good money, there was no shortage of anything. Ted had a job even if it wasn't a very good one, and I was at a Day-school I liked. The problem was learning the Lancashire dialect, spoken by everybody when not in school. It was essentially the tongue that Shakespeare spoke but the Old Man and the other Brothers found it, quite simply, incomprehensible. I had to learn it.

So there we all were, the Old Man somewhat bewildered at being a Paterfamilias again, but liking the role better, since it had no woman in it. His attitude to all women of whatever age was respectful but wary. He thought they were creatures from another world, as did most men of his age and class. He had a lot of dictums about them, mostly from literature, backed up by his experience of life. Lord Chesterfield's advice to his Son, he particularly liked: 'A man trifles with them, humours and flatters them, but he neither consults them about nor trusts them with matters of State!' . . . And, of course 'Women have, in truth, only two passions, Vanity and Love.'

Somehow, these strictures did not register with me, because I had seen a lot, maybe too much, of women in my short life, and loved rather than feared them. When the Old Man spoke to me about women, which was not often, it was always as a kind of warning. 'They are, generally speaking, trouble,' he said.

Well, nobody could dispute that.

It was simply the sort of trouble, I thought, most young men wanted. The Old Man simply saw women as people who would disrupt his life. For that reason, I think, after Marthaann he did not seek them out.

After all, one overweening obsession is enough at any one time.

'That man,' said Onkel Frank, from whose eyes the scales regarding the Old Man had long fallen, 'would skin the Aga Khan.'

'How do you mean?'

'If he had the Aga Khan's money he'd get rid of it in short order.'

'But the Aga Khan is so rich he gives away his own weight in jewels every year.'

'Even so.'

Onkel Frank's face did not flicker with a smile when he said that. He never smiled, ever. He was a kind of scholar-monk, only he had thrown out religion as the Opium of the Masses, and replaced it with Darwinism. He had read all the Rationalist writers, like Winwood Reade and Wells and Shaw, and he was soon to listen to nobody but Beethoven. He was to be seen in his Combined Room, listening to the Master on a wind-up gramophone, sixty cigarettes and a bottle of whisky in front of him, plus a large pile of dog-eared old race-cards, all dated and annotated and covered in scribbles and calculations, plus the Handicap Books, the basic tools of the Handicapper's trade. His happiness lay with the poetry of figures and mathematics and he needed nothing else: not money or women or comfort or power.

It was after a session like this that he found the Deliberate Mistake.

As he explained it to the Old Man, with me listening.

'All Race-track handicappers make one or sometimes two mistakes a Season.'

'A mistake?' echoed the Old Man.

'Possibly.'

'Or putting one in for themselves?'

'Possibly that, too.'

The Old Man nodded. If a handicapper was making a deliberate mistake, putting a winner in for himself, that was Human Nature. That is to say venal, and it could be trusted. An accident could not.

'You noticed this before?' The Old Man studied the smoke rising from his Churchman's. We were sitting in the house and the westerly sun shone in the window.

'Yes, once or twice a year. There's no money in handicapping. It's wages only.' The Old Man nodded. 'So naturally they look after themselves.' The Old Man nodded again. He understood that.

'You didn't say anything about it before?'

'No.'

'Why?'

'Nothing to say. Unless we intend to do anything about it.'

'Like what?'

'Like back it.'

The Old Man sighed. He ran his forefinger round the rim of his starched collar. 'What with?'

'I have twenty pounds,' said Onkel Frank. 'What have you?'

The Old Man ignored that question. 'What price do you think it'll make?'

'It's an animal that hasn't won much. That's why the handicapper has put it in where he has.'

'Which is?'

'Down a class. It should stand out but it won't. Most wideheads will think it's dropped down because it hasn't won many races. Or it's been ill, something like that.'

'Won't somebody else spot it?' asked the Old Man.

'They might, if they go through the card like I do.'

'Then it'll get out?'

'No. The animal hasn't won anything for six months.'

The Old Man looked startled. 'It sounds like something nobody would back with bad money.'

'That's what's clever about it.'

The Old Man shook his head in doubt. 'It sounds very iffy.'

'I'm backing it.' Onkel Frank lit one cigarette from the butt of another. 'What you do is up to you.'

The Old Man debated. 'Shall we tell Edwards?'

'No. He'd tell two or three people he owes a favour to, and that would be domino.'

The Old Man inclined his head to the truth of that.

'You're sure as sure can be that this is one the handicapper's put in for himself?'

Onkel Frank's legendary temper was not far from breaking. 'Yes, I am. Do you want in or not?'

'Certainly I want in,' said the Old Man, equably. 'The point is, what do I back it with?'

'Money, what else?'

'I haven't a lot in hand just at the moment,' said the Old Man. 'I just can't seem to get that fifty in front.'

Onkel Frank leaned forward, tapping the page of calculations in front of him. 'Hundreds. I'm talking hundreds, in
terms of profit.'

'I'd settle for fifty,' said the Old Man, 'if I had it.'

Onkel Frank's dark eyes were brimming. 'This beast will
be Six to One or I know nothing.'

'Then,' said the Old Man, 'what's the problem?'

'The problem will be backing the horse without anybody
noticing. That means putting the money on in our stocking-
feet, at the Death, with four bookies, one at each end of the
line and two in the middle.'

Onkel Frank breathed hard. He hated explaining things. 'If
the odds are only Six- or Seven-to-one, that's a hundred-and-
twenty- to a hundred-and-forty pounds profit on a twenty-
pound stake.'

The Old Man looked impressed. 'Where is it running?'

'Haydock. Saturday.'

'What about Edwards?'

'We get young Ted to clerk for him instead of me.'

'Edwards won't be very happy about that.'

'Who can you get?'

'I'll fix somebody for Virgo. We'll be back for the evening
meet, here?'

'Yes. It's the first race. We'll be off the Race-track by half-
past three.'

The Old Man regarded his Churchman's a very long
moment.

'What are we talking about here? Fifty-fifty?'

'We are not,' said Onkel Frank. 'Seventy-five, Twenty-
five.'

'Yes,' said the Old Man. 'I suppose so.'

'Bloody generous, I would say,' said Onkel Frank. 'Since

I'm only cutting you in because I can't back the animal four times on my own. Too noticeable.'

The Old Man seemed to see that. After all, he was putting nothing in and stood to win thirty or forty pounds. Still, he wasn't risking anything, and that cut down on the enjoyment. 'Yes, I suppose so.' He added, 'It's Saturday we're talking about?'

Onkel Frank nodded. Saturday was two days away.

So the bargain was struck.

Of course the Old Man could not leave it there.

The next day he despatched me to Onkel Frank's lodgings in Withnell Road with a message. 'Tell him I'm putting a tenner in myself.'

'Just that?'

'Just that.'

I wanted to ask where the ten pounds had come from, but there was no need. He told me.

'I got an advance from Ken Virgo against wages.'

Ken Virgo, his employer, was winning an astonishing amount of money at the Dogs, Making a Book. Too much. I had heard the Old Man say there had to be a rabbit away somewhere.

I took that to mean Ken Virgo was slightly too clever in some way.

'But why wager anything when you don't need to?' I asked.

A foolish question. I should have known better.

'You know what Gladstone said?'

'What?'

'There is nothing in cards unless the family plate is at stake.'

'This isn't cards.'

'No, but the principle holds, you see.'

I didn't, but I didn't argue.

Onkel Frank was surprised by my visit.

Not half as surprised as I was.

I had never seen him with a lady before.

Nowadays, one would say woman. In those days to say woman was not refined or proper. The word woman meant somebody Working Class.

Onkel Frank introduced her, looking somewhat embarrassed, as Mrs Florrie Ogden.

A Missus? Where was her husband? I wondered.

But Florrie had divination. 'I'm a widow, you see. I know I'm young for it but there you are, you can't pick your time to go, can you, you never know the day nor the hour and what's your name, young man? Oh, I do think he looks like you, Frank.'

Florrie was a peroxide-blonde, as they used to say then, and perhaps only thirty years old, and wore bright lipstick that left a red mark on her cigarette and the rim of the glass from which she was drinking her gin and lime, without, of course, ice.

Gin and lime was thought a very fast drink. Florrie was still talking. Her skirt, I noticed, was very short and showed a lot of silken leg.

'Oh, I expect you're surprised, young man, to see somebody, well, a lady, in your Uncle's room, but we're really quite good friends, aren't we, Frankie?'

I had never heard anybody, man or woman, call Onkel Frank Frankie.

'Did you have a message for me?' he asked, testily.

'Yes.'

'What is it?'

'My Father says he'll have ten tomorrow.'

Onkel Frank nodded as if he wasn't surprised to hear it. 'Tell him all right.'

I turned to go. There didn't seem anything to stay for. Florrie wiggled her fingers. 'See you again soon, Sonny Boy.'

I bobbed my head and escaped.

Onkel Frank followed me to the front door. He put a florin in my hand.

'And not a word. Understand?'

I knew he meant the Old Man. I nodded and went off up the street.

The Old Man and Onkel Frank went to Haydock Park and backed the Deliberate Mistake (an animal called *Arctic Star*) and came home rejoicing.

Nobody in the Family was prepared for the Old Man's sudden generosity. Not that he wasn't generous at any time. He was: it was one of the good things about him; that and the fact that he never expected anything of anybody. It was the fact that to be generous you needed to be holding folding.

Now, here he was buying Ted a new suit and shirts and ties, and myself a grey flannel suit and shoes and even the School items I hadn't yet bought, such as a schoolbag and my own football, and last of all a pair of Mansfield Hotspur boots costing thirty-five shillings. They were of the best and softest leather and had special protectors to ward off ankle-taps. There was no need to stand in water wearing them until they were soft, or to do much more than dubbin them.

He also bought me a Wally Hammond cricket-bat. I have it yet. Nobody ever throws a cricket-bat away.

Even Jane got money for a set of new underclothes. There was no sign of them, as there wouldn't be. Jane was a Victorian and wore a shift (a long cotton garment) under her corsets, as women had done for three hundred years. No shop-assistant today would know what a shift was. Also, the Old Man gave her twenty pounds in cash for provisions for the house (usually he would give her five pounds a week for everything) and bought in a stock of drink and personally purchased his favourite delicacies: Gentleman's Relish, Van Houten's Cocoa, William Cooper's Marmalade and a quantity of ripe Gorgonzola cheese, which he would eat, often with a raw Spanish onion and a large cup of cocoa, at the end of a long day, after the evening's racing.

It was the only meal he seemed to have time for.

Anything more formal oppressed him. He would be finished and on his feet while others were still eating.

'Percy, you'll get indigestion,' said Jane.

But he didn't.

Also, he never ever sat in an easy chair. He was, as Onkel Frank remarked, still behaving as if he was twenty-five years of age. To me then, as now, that seemed a sensible thing to do. If you could do it.

If Onkel Frank had made as much money out of the Deliberate Mistake as the Old Man had, you would not have known it. He would appear at the house, as usual, around six o'clock in the evening, in time to walk to the Greyhound Track with the Old Man and Ted, if he was free of his duties in Edwards' office. Ted had something of the Brothers in him. An interest in the mad, bad world of Dogs and Horses. The Methodism that had rubbed off on me had not affected him. He seemed to enjoy it all, and was now a sporter of plus-fours and spats and had hankerings for a motor-bike. Ted was good-looking and easy-going and protected me in all sorts of ways. I admired him but wondered if he was being wise, getting into such doubtless sinful things as gambling and smoking and sometimes even drinking. The Old Man greeted these early signs of what Marthaann and Isaac would have thought a dissolute way of life with unspoken approval. He had a new disciple.

Not that Ted was a foolish gambler. Cool and thoughtful, he was like, if anybody, Edwards.

Onkel Frank, who had been a father-figure to him in all kinds of ways (the Old Man being absent in the Army and so on), was not a real gambler. He knew the odds against any wager. It was only when something like the Deliberate Mistake happened that he, so to speak, got into the Game.

Now, he was In the Money.

But, as I say, nobody would have known it.

Long after the Old Man's winnings had gone (and his losses must have been spectacular to get rid of it in the time he did), Onkel Frank was behaving pretty much the same. That is to say, as irascible as ever and unforgiving of any kind of sloppy thinking, even by me. I had developed a habit of testing political theories on him.

'The Labour Party would get rid of Unemployment.'

He shook his head. 'No chance. Two reasons. One, they won't get in again, short of war. Two, they are half of them Pacifists, and a look across the Channel should tell them what use that is.'

'Hitler?'

'Naturally. The man puts Pacifists in the Army.'

'What if they won't go?'

'Jail. Worse. He's the Danger.'

In Racing Terms the 'Danger' is the Dog or Horse that might beat the Favourite. It seemed to just about sum up Adolf Hitler and his regime.

'Only Churchill will do anything, and they don't want him,' he added.

'Everybody says he's a Warmonger.'

'Good job he is. Somebody has to be.'

Said the Old Man, 'Frank is very warlike so long as he isn't doing the fighting.'

'How so?'

'In the War he was called up for the Army and put in a room with two hundred other recruits, but not yet sworn in. He left that room and walked down the street to the naval recruiting office and joined the Navy. The Navy is the Senior Service, so they had first call on him. He went back to the Army people and showed them his Navy acceptance slip, and they let him go.'

'Why did he do that?'

'He said to the man next to him, "Everybody in this room will be dead in six months' time." He was right. They were.'

'Did the Navy get him?'

'No. By the time they called him up he was in the Shipyards, due to Isaac Henderson's influence. He was in a Reserved Occupation.'

'What was he doing?'

'Supposed to be Isaac's helper, but he has no head for heights, so they put him in the Stores.' The Old Man puffed on his Churchman's. 'That is how he spent the War. So he's in no position to tell anybody else to go and fight Adolf Hitler.'

'Maybe not, but is he right?'

'On these sort of things he's always right.' The Old Man sighed. 'That does not prevent him from being an arrant coward.'

The Old Man demolished many people that way. Well, he was in a position to do it.

Oddly enough, Onkel Frank did not seem any kind of coward. His opinions were unpopular but he would persist in them, talking down all the nay-sayers in pubs and clubs who felt that Neville Chamberlain was the answer. Onkel Frank hissed him when he appeared on the screen at the Waterloo Picture House holding his pathetic piece of paper. A young man in the row in front objected, saying, 'Do you want War?'

Onkel Frank replied by snapping his fingers in the young man's face. 'You'll be in a German Labour Camp in two years unless you fight him!'

Everybody told Onkel Frank to shut up.

That, I thought, was hardly the action of an arrant coward. It impressed me, but I wasn't so sure I wanted a War. Not, anyway, for a while. I was too likely to be in it. And I had read *All Quiet on the Western Front* and *The Road Back* and *Education Before Verdun* and *Goodbye to All That*, to ready myself for it, just in case. Most of us had.

But nobody old wanted War. They remembered the last one too well.

So, Onkel Frank went about his daily tasks, reading all the newspapers and arguing with people he didn't know about the French and the Poles and the Communists and Hitler.

He found few takers and those sadly misinformed about the world situation.

'The man,' said the Old Man, 'is certifiably fokkin insane.'

Indeed, the Family name for Onkel Frank was 'Barmy'.

Too much thinking, it was agreed, had turned his brain. He was given to fits of temper, hated heights, and had been known to leave Race-tracks because of incipient thunderstorms, which he hated. This kind of behaviour was unknown in Racing Circles.

'He has always been the same,' reported the Old Man. 'He's an unmitigated disaster in any sort of enterprise needing calm.'

'Just the same,' I pointed out, 'he still seems to have the money he won at Haydock Park.'

'Yes,' said the Old Man pensively. 'And much good does it do him. It's in the Bank.'

'Gaining interest?' I pointed out.

'To what purpose?' asked the Old Man, and put on his hat and went out to the Dogs.

But Onkel Frank sprang a surprise.

He announced that he was getting married.

'The man,' said the Old Man, 'has taken leave of his fokkin senses.'

Nobody except me knew who Florrie was.

But investigation soon proved to them that she was a young widow (sharp intake of breath from the Old Man on hearing this), and had been working lately in a cake-shop.

The Old Man said it for everybody. 'I always knew the man was batchy but now he has proven it without restriction.'

Of course, none of this was said to Onkel Frank's face.

First, there had to be a Family meeting with Florrie.

Jane, after consideration, put on a High Tea the next Sunday. Everybody was there to meet her except Edwards, who had received the news with amusement but stayed away on principle. He never ever did anything social with the rest of the Family, which preserved his status.

Florrie arrived, dressed, as they said, to the nines.

Everybody was astonished by her.

It was plain, before she had been in the Front Room for ten minutes, that despite her appearance she was smart. Her voice was unashamed mid-Lancashire and her vowels, in consequence, were all over the place. Well, they would be, since she came from Padiham, a small town in the Ribblesdale Valley, and her parents and her grandparents had worked in the Cotton Mills, where the women all had loud voices, born of shouting to each other across the spinning-machines and general noise. She was, I thought, likeable, because she was unaffected and direct, if somewhat given to uninhibited squeals of laughter and a generally happy view of life.

To Ted and Jane and the Old Man, of course, she simply looked and sounded a jolly enough young woman, but taking a lot for granted. That is how people thought then. What you were was nothing like as important as who you were. And Florrie, who could probably have got hold of almost anybody (of like background to herself, in Blackpool), had picked on somebody so plainly unsuited to her that even I could see it.

The reason?

Well, plainly the company thought, as they ate their way through boiled ham and tomatoes and lettuce and home-made custard-tarts and pints of hot, sweet tea, that it was the Ring.

The Ring was a large garnet, and it rested on her engagement finger. 'How a woman can have an engagement ring when she's a widow-woman, I don't know,' said Jane later. I was only glad that my sister Peggy was absent. Peggy would have found it all very funny.

I didn't know enough to know why, but I was sorry for Onkel Frank. He fussed around Florrie, offering her cakes and tea and generally behaving in a very un-Onkel Frank way.

'Besotted,' said the Old Man afterwards. 'The man is plainly besotted.'

'Well,' said Jane, 'it's his choice, Percy.'

'And a thunderingly bad one,' said the Old Man.

Nobody contradicted him.

For Florrie had talked all the time that she was in the house. We had heard at length about her family and friends in Padiham, their doings being related in breathless detail, and we had heard about the last hours of her dead husband, a postman, who had died of the consumption. The Old Man's face was as stone as he listened politely to these – to him – painful and unnecessary facts.

'I wonder,' said Florrie, innocently, 'why Frank has never married before?'

'Well, he courted a woman for sixteen years,' said the Old Man.

'Nothing like sixteen,' said Onkel Frank. 'Possibly six.'

'Until,' said the Old Man, 'her father asked him his intentions.'

'I should think so!' exclaimed Florrie with a saucy sidelong look at Onkel Frank, who remained impassive.

'This is not a time for marriage,' said Onkel Frank. 'A European War in the offing!'

'Then why do it?' asked the Old Man, sotto voce.

The question hung in the air and remained unanswered.

Florrie outlined the plans for the wedding which was to take place in the local Register Office. 'Everybody's invited, you know! We want as many of Frankie's family as possible; he says money's no object, so we're having the reception at Dickinson's Restaurant, in their upstairs room, and they do put on a very nice do, I must say that for them, nowt like tea's been here today, I know, but special and fancy-like for weddings, and I'm havin' a new costume made in navy blue, I like navy blue, and there'll be drink for them as want it and tea and lemonade for them as doesn't, and all in all it should be a very Nice Do!'

Her face shone under the powder and paint and it was easy to see how happy she was. Onkel Frank hovered, solicitous, proud.

It was, as the Old Man said, an astonishing turn-up.

After Florrie had gone, kissing everybody, even me, and declaring what a good time she had had, the Old Man sat down to have the Postmortem.

'How could it possibly happen?' asked Ted. 'I mean, something must have brought the whole thing on? Onkel Frank has always been against marriage. He doesn't believe in it, he's said so a thousand times.'

The Old Man was silent for a long moment, then reasoned. 'For a thing like this to have happened, he had to have money. To get mixed up with Florrie at all, he had to have money, enough to knock him, however temporarily, off his trolley.'

I waited.

We all waited.

The Old Man, as ever, spoke with the tongues of angels.

'It was that Deliberate Mistake that did it! There cannot be a shadow of doubt about that!'

And that was why Onkel Frank, Thinker and Rationalist, not to say Freethinker, married Dorothy Ogden, widow, at fifty-five years of age.

Nobody, this time, challenged the Old Man's final verdict that he was, without fear of contradiction, Certifiably Fokkin Insane.

Inside a couple of years, Onkel Frank had a couple of daughters. He went back to handicapping, at a Dog-track in

Yorkshire, but owing to his total honesty (described by the Old Man as total insanity) he lost the job for refusing to 'put a dog or two in' for the proprietors of the Dog-track. That is, to cheat. Back in Blackpool, he resumed clerking for Edwards, and rented a semi-detached house, with a garden and an apple tree. I went to see him and he showed me round. Florrie was in the kitchen, singing cheerfully to the radio music of Henry Hall and obviously happy. The children gambolled on the lawn, in the sun.

I asked him how life was treating him.

He gazed around at the cosy domestic scene. 'As you can see, I'm carrying Top Weight.'

It was a handicapper's answer.

The Baby Snatcher

It was probably the Lindbergh case that gave the Baby Snatcher his name. That, plus the fact that he seemed to have a good deal of money. Which, so bad was the Game, had to come from something dramatic, like – perhaps? – a ransom.

The fact was, the Old Man knew nothing about him at all. Not even his real name, which was certainly not Smith, the one he offered us for general use. Somebody at the Dog-track said that he had been in jail for kidnapping, but nobody really believed that. Nobody kidnapped anybody for ransom in England in those days. Nobody else would have had the money to pay it.

'Apart from that,' the Old Man summed up to Onkel Frank and Ted, after the cheese-and-cocoa supper that ended all their days after racing, 'the man is a total mystery. Nobody knows anything about him.'

'Not unusual for this place,' said Ted. 'Everybody comes from some other place.'

It was true. Many unemployed men walked the Pennines to get to Blackpool. It was rumoured that there was money in the town. There was certainly none anywhere else.

'The point is,' the Old Man persisted, 'he seems to have money. However he got it.'

Ted asked, 'He can't be a real Baby Snatcher, can he?'

'Unlikely,' said the Old Man, impatiently. 'Whatever he is, I repeat, he has Ready Cash he wants to invest in the Book.'

There was instant silence and total attention at this statement. It was now Winter and the downside (as they would say today) of the Dogs was that nobody came to Blackpool during the Winter months. There were now only three meetings a week, Monday, Friday and Saturday, attended by locals. It had cut down on wages and thus on general prosperity for everybody.

'Will he want to Make a Book at the Dogs?' asked Onkel Frank.

'I have put him off that,' replied the Old Man.

'Why?'

'Because there's no profit there for a Bookie. Everybody's pulling their prices to get any sort of money in the Bag. Even Edwards is losing money, or anyway not winning any!'

Onkel Frank and Ted nodded to the truth of that.

'What,' asked Onkel Frank, 'is the proposition?'

'We make a Book at Haydock Park next weekend.'

'What with?'

'What he puts in the Bag.'

'Plus?'

The Old Man hesitated. 'Whatever *we* put in.'

Onkel Frank lit a cigarette. 'That won't be much.'

'He's not to know that,' said the Old Man.

Onkel Frank persisted. 'What kind of money has he got?'

'I don't think he'll worry about fifty pounds.'

'Fifty?' said Onkel Frank, disbelievingly. 'Has he *got* fifty?'

'He says so, and I believe him.'

'Possibly the man *is* a Baby Snatcher, after all?'

Onkel Frank's remark was serious, but the Old Man and Ted just laughed.

The Old Man said, 'We'll need a Joint. And a Bag.'

A Joint was (and is) a Bookie's Board and Stand, marked with his name. It is in two pieces and joins together. A Bag is the large leather receptacle to hold the money, if any.

'And the Book,' said Onkel Frank.

'Of course.'

'No problem there,' said Onkel Frank. 'Edwards has a spare Joint and Bag. I can borrow that.'

'It will mean him knowing,' said the Old Man.

'Not necessarily.'

The Old Man nodded. 'What about transport? We need a car.'

Ted said, 'I can borrow one from Harry Budd.' Harry was a local chauffeur with a tolerant employer. 'He'll let me have it for the day for a pound or two.'

'Then we're off to the Races,' said the Old Man.

But Onkel Frank's eyes never left him. 'Who will Make the Book?'

'I will,' said the Old Man. 'Who else?'

Onkel Frank shook his head but said nothing.

'You can clerk and go through the Card in advance. You'll mark the Card for me. All I'll do is follow your advice.'

'Yes,' said Onkel Frank. 'If you do!'

'Of course I will,' said the Old Man. 'I've done it before.'

'Not too successfully,' said Onkel Frank.

Onkel Frank and Ted exchanged glances but said no more. The Old Man looked irritated. 'This is a Gift Horse. The

Baby Snatcher has fifty pounds to put in. We, in theory, need fifty between us.'

He was looking at Onkel Frank.

Onkel Frank took a swallow of his scaldingly hot cocoa. 'No possibility of fifty?'

'Twenty or less might suffice, if it's in oncers.'

The Old Man meant pound notes.

'It won't,' said Onkel Frank, 'if he knows what he's doing.'

'That is the point,' said the Old Man, losing patience. 'He doesn't know what he's doing, that's the whole point of the exercise.'

Said Ted, greatly daring, 'Are we going to Haydock to genuinely Make a Book or are we going to Haydock to part the Baby Snatcher from his money?'

The Old Man looked shocked at the suggestion. 'We simply hope to show a profit on the day, no more and no less.'

'With only his fifty in the Bag?' Ted persisted.

'Plus what we put in.'

'Which will be?'

'What we can. Say, twenty?'

And there it rested.

The Haydock Meeting was on a Saturday, so I could go.

Ted was driving the Rover, borrowed for the day. Ted could drive anything, from a motor-bike to a lorry. He wasn't wearing his plus-fours or his spats that day, but a tweed suit and a Van Heusen shirt. His fair hair shone with brilliantine, Yardley's Lavender. The Old Man used it, and so did the Brothers. I used it too, taken from Ted's jar.

The Old Man packed the Joint in the boot of the car, and we were ready for off. Onkel Frank was already sitting in front with Ted, gazing moodily at the sky in case of thunder.

86

I had heard him saying to Ted, *sotto*, 'The only thing that worries me is that man's certainty he's a Bookie. He'll never be a Bookie while he has a hole in his arse.'

Ted had replied, 'Oh, I don't know. There won't be all that much money flying about. And you can keep him straight.'

'Even so.'

Said the Old Man cheerfully, sitting in the back of the Rover, 'I have a feeling we are going to charge the punters today.'

The Baby Snatcher was waiting for us outside the Waterloo Hotel. He was a disappointment. I was expecting somebody sinister, rather like Hauptmann, the kidnapper of the Lindberg child, with thick pebble glasses and a German accent. The Baby Snatcher turned out to be a mild-looking, rubicund man in his thirties with a pair of gold-rimmed glasses and no hat. He wore a neat brown suit and a raincoat. He could have been a bank-clerk. He did not look capable of snatching a handbag, never mind a baby.

'Morning, Percy. Frank. Ted.' To me, he nodded and smiled.

He got in the car next to the Old Man. 'Everything all right, Percy?'

Said the Old Man, 'Everything Tickety-Boo. Are we ready for off?'

Ted put the car in gear and we droned off down the Preston New Road.

The Baby Snatcher read the sporting pages of the *Daily Chronicle* in silence for a while.

'Frank's been through the Card for us,' said the Old Man.

'Good,' said the Baby Snatcher, genially. 'That's good work, Frank. It'll be very valuable.'

Onkel Frank grunted.

'Ted will be Floorman,' said the Old Man.

'Good, good, excellent,' replied the Baby Snatcher, beaming. 'And Percy will be Making a Book, on the stool, as it were?'

He even talked like a Bank Clerk.

The Old Man nodded. 'Of course. I'll keep you posted how things are going, race by race.'

'Excellent, splendid,' said the Baby Snatcher, with another beam, showing two rows of false teeth. 'I think we're well-prepared, yes, exceedingly well-prepared.'

Onkel Frank grunted in total disgust.

Ted said nothing.

The Old Man lit a Churchman's and I stared out of the car window all the way to the Race-track. It was mostly shuttered shops and Unemployed men hanging about on street corners. The Old Man kept up a line of chat about the Book always winning, if you gave it time. That was insurance-talk, I realised, against the possibility, unspoken but dreaded by all, that it might not win this time out.

I kept waiting for the Baby Snatcher to ask about money, but he never did.

As we came into Haydock town, he took an envelope from his pocket and said, 'I think you'll find there's fifty pounds in there, Percy.'

It was in the Old Man's inside pocket, as they say, as if by magic. 'Ours is already in the Bag,' he said. Well, twenty pounds was.

The Baby Snatcher nodded his head vigorously. 'Of course. I'm looking forward to this, Percy, the first of many, you know. Oh yes, the first of many.'

It was then I realised that the Baby Snatcher was a Wide Mug. A Wide Mug is a person who knows something about how the Game works but not as much as he thinks he does. I had heard the Old Man say that the Baby Snatcher had lost a lot of money to the Bookies and was looking to get some of it back. 'Since he's lost a lot, he thinks everybody else has. He thinks the Book wins every time.'

'Then he's a Wide Mug,' said Onkel Frank.

That was, anyway, one mystery solved, the why and wherefore of the Baby Snatcher investing in the Book at all.

'Patsy Black!' explained the Old Man. He shouted through the window. 'Patsy? Want a lift to the Track?' Adding, 'Stop the car!'

Ted sighed, and stopped dead.

All around the car, filling the pavements of the small Northern town, were the hopeful racegoers. Down-at-heel and be-capped, walking to the racecourse from the Railway Station, these were the punters who had come on the train, those characterised by the Old Man as the needy and the greedy. They certainly looked needy. Anybody with any real money would travel by car.

The man called Patsy Black, who was wearing a straw boater with a faded ribbon round it, was examining the Old Man's offer with some surprise. He was a thickset Glaswegian, answering aptly to the German description of the breed: a poison dwarf. It was true that the slum-dwellers of that great city were, in those days, an average of five-foot-four in height. Usually they made up for it in pugnacity.

'Is there any room inside?' Patsy asked, doubtfully. The Old Man opened the door and Patsy squeezed in. There wasn't room, really, but Patsy seemed grateful. It was a two-mile walk to the Race-track.

'Hoo air ye, Percy?' he asked, nodding to the others and ignoring me. 'Ye're in the money, ah see?'

'Just keeping afloat,' said the Old Man.

'It's a bastard of a season,' said Patsy Black. 'Do ye have anything for the meetin' at all?'

'Nothing,' said the Old Man, 'that I can recommend, no.'

'Frank?' asked Patsy Black.

'Nothing.'

'Ah. Weel.' Patsy Black lit a cigar that looked as if it had seen better days. 'Ah dinna have a thing masel' either. All ma sources are dried up. I tell ye, it's criminal these days. Ye canny trust the trainers nivver mind the bleedin' jockeys!'

The Baby Snatcher laid down his *Daily Chronicle*. 'Droopy Drawers in the fourth is, I believe, one to watch.'

Patsy Black looked at him like a drowning man given a lifebelt. 'Is it noo? Is it?'

Patsy Black was already looking at his Form Book, a crumpled and tattered copy, and his Race-card for the day, obviously obtained in advance.

'It's form looks a wee bit off?'

The Baby Snatcher shook his head. 'Very well-fancied, I understand, Sir.'

Patsy Black nodded briskly, put away his Race-card, and nodded his thanks as the Rover turned into the car-park.

'Who's that?' Ted asked, as Patsy Black trudged away in the crowd of punters moving towards the turnstiles.

'He's one of the old Professional Backers,' said the Old Man. 'He's been in the Game for fifty years. He must be seventy-five years of age.'

'He can't be very good, can he?' Ted began to get the Joint out of the boot. 'If he's been a lifetime at it and he's still walking to the Track.'

'Patsy's had his ups and downs, but who hasn't?'

The Old Man was always on the side of the underdog. For obvious reasons.

Onkel Frank however was asking the Baby Snatcher a question.

'What was the name of that animal again?'

The Baby Snatcher told him.

Onkel Frank looked at his Race-card. I could see his marks. 'One' against the horse he thought would win. 'D' for 'Danger' against the horse most likely to beat it, if anything could. He mused as he looked, uttered the words, 'I can't see it,' and led the procession towards the Bookies' Entrance.

The Old Man pressed the large leather bag into my hands.

'Hold it tight,' he said loudly. 'There's money in there.'

The Baby Snatcher beamed, showing his pot-teeth. 'Yes, we want it full by the end of today's racing, don't we?'

Since nobody else said anything, I replied, 'Yes, we do, Sir.'

'Good lad,' the Baby Snatcher replied, and presented me with a half-crown.

The Old Man sighed in relief. Obviously the Baby Snatcher was of a trusting nature. Such people earned the Old Man's highest praise. Ken Virgo, his carefree employer at the Dogs, had earned it. 'Ken is a White Man!'

Now, I could see that the Baby Snatcher had entered that rare category. In the Racing Game, few qualified.

The Old Man and Onkel Frank and Ted went through the formalities of paying Bookies' fees and registering, and finally they carried the Joint out to the Silver Ring, the cheapest part of the Course, where the Admission Fee did not exceed five shillings and where most bets were in florins and half-crowns – that is to say, in silver coinage. Their allotted stand, as newcomers who had booked late, was at the very end of the line of Bookies, some of whom were already standing and chatting, in groups. They were mostly flashily dressed and had a defeated look about them. Many of their boards bore the wary slogan: 'Member BPA'. That meant they were members of the Bookmakers' Protection Association. This had been founded, the Old Man had told me, to reassure the public against the Razor Gangs who had terrorised the tracks for many years. All that had stopped abruptly when a Lord Chief Justice had handed out sentences of seven or ten years (every day to be served) plus twelve lashes with the Cat-o'-nine-tails a fortnight after the offender went to jail, and another twelve lashes a fortnight before he came out.

Not surprisingly, it had put paid to the Razor Gangs, as the Old Man said. Nowadays, such a thing would be thought brutal, but nobody questioned it then. On the contrary.

Their Boards also proclaimed the legend: 'Prompt Payment and Civility.'

This was because (the Old Man had told me) some Bookies were abusive when asked to pay out large sums to punters, and had been known to issue a dreadful curse with every bank-note they parted with. This was thought bad practice but was by no means stamped out.

Welshing, or Doing a Runner, likewise.

The Old Man often repeated the old Race-track adage: 'A Bookie has to Welsh three times before he's learned enough to Make a Book.'

These thoughts did not reassure me. I knew that Onkel Frank and Ted thought the Old Man an incompetent Bookie; that much was obvious to me.

That the Old Man thought they were wrong was equally obvious. He stood on the stool, best Woodrow hat on head,

Fusiliers' tie knotted into gleaming, white-starched collar, and faced the indifferent punters with total confidence.

Onkel Frank stood behind him, cigarette in mouth, the Book crooked in his arm. Ted went along the line of Bookies, getting them used to seeing him so that they knew he was a Floorman and not a punter.

The Baby Snatcher was standing behind Onkel Frank, leaning on the rails, his gold-rimmed spectacles glinting in the sun. He had a proprietorial air about him.

The punters stood in a living, regimented mass, their noise registering as a loud buzz, not unlike that of bees about to come out of the hive. Except (I thought) that it was the punters who were probably going to get stung. Apart perhaps from Patsy Black, no doubt somewhere amongst them. A Professional Backer like Patsy relied for his tips on the stable-lads and jockeys and trainers, sometimes even Owners. He laid money on horses for them and put some on for himself as well.

Professional Backers, the Old Man opined, were a race apart. Their knowledge was encyclopaedic and their nerves of steel. Patsy Black seemed to fit none of these descriptions, but obviously he once had. It was all very puzzling.

Suddenly, the Bookies started to shout.

Somewhere, far off, across the crowds and the greensward of the Track, away under the Big Stand, next to Tattersall's, the Horses were parading around, under the eyes of the Owners, Trainers, and those exalted, God-like beings, the Stewards of the Course. Here, in the Silver Ring, all that might just as well have been happening on the moon.

Here all that happened was that the Bookies began to shout and the punters ignored them, standing, undecided, waiting to see what prices would be on offer. The punters were like

Zulu impi and the Bookies like the Welsh at Yorke's Drift, profoundly outnumbered but brave.

The Old Man chalked up his first price. Three-to-One against what was to turn out to be the Favourite.

He did not seem to see Ted waving his arms wildly, or Onkel Frank peering round from behind him to see what he had done.

Too late! The Old Man had taken six or seven bets before Onkel Frank's obvious rage persuaded him to rub the price out with a wet forefinger.

The punters fell back, the luckiest of them holding the tickets the Old Man had given them like trophies of war, which in a way they were.

Ted looked at Onkel Frank, exchanged a word, then went back down the line, as the other Bookies began to take bets and the prices changed, reflecting the money for each horse. The Favourite's price shortened, until it was even money, where it remained until the Off. And then it won the race by several lengths.

'Would you credit it?' asked the Old Man audibly, paying out pound notes and silver to the punters who had rushed in when he first put up the price of Three to One on his Board. As far as I could see he had not laid any other animal at all, and therefore had lost money on the race without the possibility of winning any.

Onkel Frank engaged the Old Man in a furious but muted altercation, seemingly unnoticed by the Baby Snatcher, who only came forward once, to enquire how things were going. They reassured him with words and mime and he went back, still smiling, to his position on the rails.

It went on like that all afternoon.

The end of racing found the Old Man gazing at an empty

Bag. In fact, he didn't bet on the last race at all, closing the Bag abruptly before the punters could place any more disastrous bets. I stood on the rails with the Baby Snatcher, watching the horses flash by in a thunder of hooves and colour, and listened to the long sad sigh of the Mug Punters as their choices went down.

The Old Man, walking towards the Bookies' quarters, put as good a face on events as possible.

'Would you believe it?' he asked the world. 'Every Favourite walks home, except two! The odds against that happening you couldn't put on paper!'

Ted and Onkel Frank merely nodded and looked irritated.

The Baby Snatcher did not seem too despondent for a man who had lost a considerable amount of cash.

'It's the way it goes, Percy,' he offered. 'There's always another day.'

The Old Man brightened at this. 'Yes. There is. Nothing went our way today. It couldn't happen again in a million years.'

Ted and Onkel Frank wordlessly lugged the Joint and I carried the empty Bag to the Rover.

'There's one thing,' said the Old Man, 'we're away before the rush.'

'Yes, indeed,' said the Baby Snatcher, his glasses glinting in the dying rays of the wintry sun. 'It's been a good day out.'

Ted and Onkel Frank looked at him as if he was mad.

The Rover was almost the first car out of the car-park. As we turned on to the main road, the Old Man said, 'There's Patsy again!'

Ted stopped the car and Patsy Black got in. He looked dusty and in some way defeated, and squeezed into a space next to the Baby Snatcher, expelling his alcoholic and tobacco-laden breath as he did so. Nobody showed disapproval or discomfort. All men drank and smoked to excess then, the only ones who didn't, as the Old Man would say, being those who, for financial reasons, couldn't.

'What sort of a day hae ye had, Percy?' asked Patsy Black.

'Very average,' replied the Old Man. 'Extremely average.'

Well, it was one way of describing a disaster.

'Sorry tae hear it.' Patsy Black drew on his foul cigar, which could have been the one he had been smoking four hours before. 'I spewed my cash, what I had.'

'Well,' said the Old Man courteously, 'I would have thought you'd be on a favourite or two?'

Patsy Black considered that. 'Aye, I would. But I took notice of what this gentleman here gave me and I had a decent bet on Droopy Drawers.' His voice held nothing but mild disappointment. 'If it came well-recommended to y'self,' he said agreeably enough to the Baby Snatcher, 'then that's the way it goes. Ye were guid enough tae pass on to me a piece of your own information, I knew I was in guid company, so I had a bet on it and it went down and there it is, isn't it, noo?'

The Old Man made to make a comment, but he was too late.

The Baby Snatcher was replying. 'Yes, Droopy Drawers was very well recommended in the *Daily Chronicle* this morning. Gimcrack gave it his Best Bet of the Day.'

There was an awful silence in the car.

It lasted a long time.

Patsy Black, when he spoke, seemed to be having trouble with his voice. 'Ye took the tip from the newspaper?'

'I always follow Gimcrack,' said the Baby Snatcher.

The next thing anybody knew, Patsy Black had him by the throat.

'Give me a tip from the paper! Are ye fokkin mad?'

Ted stopped the car.

The Old Man gripped Patsy Black's wrists. They were as steel.

Ted opened the rear door and pulled Patsy Black off the Baby Snatcher, and deposited him in the road. Then he got back in the car and drove off. Patsy Black stood in the road and cursed us, audibly.

Nobody inside spoke.

Even the Old Man seemed lost for words.

The Baby Snatcher coughed a few times to clear his throat. Onkel Frank silently offered him a flask of whisky. The Baby Snatcher shook his head. 'I never touch spirits, Frank, thank you for the kind thought.'

Onkel Frank put the flask wordlessly back in his hip-pocket.

The Baby Snatcher inspected his glasses and polished them. 'I must say, that was totally uncalled for.'

Nobody answered.

At last the Old Man summed up the day, under his breath and to himself, but audible to all. 'An unmitigated fokkin disaster!'

The Baby Snatcher was not keen, the Old Man later reported, on further investment in a Book. Nor, for that matter, were they, since they had (the Old Man and Onkel Frank) put ten pounds each in the Bag and lost it.

As Onkel Frank said to Ted, 'He has no idea how to Make a Book and never had. No talent for it, simple as that.'

It was to Onkel Frank that the Baby Snatcher turned next.

He discovered that Onkel Frank had a marked-card before each Meeting at the Dog-track. He made a point of asking him what he fancied and backing it. Over a period he showed a profit, and was to be seen collecting small amounts of money from the Bookies, an innocent smile on his face.

Once he had twenty pounds to collect from Johnny Tye, a renowned Irish Bookie, who worked on a short fuse and did not like losing twenty pounds to a Mug. Tye paid him in pound notes, cursing him for a cross-eyed git (and nineteen other obscene things) every time he put a note in the Baby Snatcher's palm. He did not repeat himself once. The Baby Snatcher smiled blandly all the time.

Why not? He was collecting. And he always gave Onkel Frank twenty per cent of his winnings, if any. 'A very fair man, the Baby Snatcher,' said Onkel Frank, unused to such treatment.

The Baby Snatcher, for a season, became one of the family. He would appear at the house before racing and walk up to the Dog-track with the Old Man. He would drink nothing stronger than the odd cup of tea or cocoa, and never accepted anything to eat. Old Jane would press him to a scone or a slice of apple tart but he would never take it. The Old Man said he was living in rooms somewhere near the Waterloo Hotel, and that he would occasionally have a bet on the Crown Green Bowling competitions there. Nobody had ever seen him with a woman. He never spoke of any family or gave out any details of his life before he had appeared in Blackpool. He spoke only of horses and dogs and their chances of winning or losing and seemed to think of little else, and that was enough in the company of the Old Man and Onkel Frank, who thought of little else either, and were anyway always ready to discuss such topics. The odd thing was, the Baby Snatcher didn't really win much money racing but he never seemed to be short of it. He was to be seen, neatly dressed and brilliantined, standing in the Silver End at the Dogs, taking losses and wins in the same even, good-tempered manner.

Then suddenly he disappeared.

Nobody thought anything of it for a while.

Then the Old Man found out by divers means exactly where he had been staying, and came back with a strange and disturbing story. 'His landlady told me that two men in hats came to the door and took him away, or so she said. He didn't leave anything except his shirts and ties and a jacket and there's nothing in the pockets to say where she should send them.'

Onkel Frank digested that.

'Lifted?' he enquired.

'Almost certainly,' said the Old Man. 'But for what?'

'The Baby Snatching charge?'

'Who knows?'

The Old Man made further enquiries of his friend Sergeant Bragg of the local Constabulary (a member of the gambling fraternity) but he was unable to help. 'If they wanted him they'd just take him, Percy. They shouldn't, but it's what they'd do if it was a Serious Charge.'

An eye was kept on the National newspapers, but there was nothing reported. Everybody was sorry to hear he might be in trouble. He was a quiet man who kept himself to himself and was accordingly liked. Slowly, we all stopped talking and speculating about him.

I did not see him again for several years.

It happened in a street in Brussels in 1945 and I was in the RAF. I noticed a man who looked familiar going into a bar.

I followed him in, and in the darkness of the place I wondered, as he turned, if I might be mistaken. He was wearing khaki and was a sergeant in the Royal Artillery. He still wore glasses but of the steely Forces-issue, but he looked thinner and harder, as everybody did in those years.

'I think I know you,' I said.

He looked at me steadily. 'I don't think so.'

I was nonplussed.

'Blackpool? The Dogs? Percy? Frank? That day at the Races at Haydock Park?'

He looked at me for what seemed a very long time.

'No. You've got the wrong person.'

He didn't say 'bloke', or 'fella' or 'chap'.

He said 'person'. In a gentle voice. Nobody, in a War, has a gentle voice.

'You do remember me?' I pressed.

The rubicund face beamed. The pot-teeth were the same. 'Sorry. You meet a lot of people in a war, you know. You're mistaken, I'm afraid.'

And he walked out into the Boulevard Adolfe Max without a backward glance and was lost in the crowds of soldiers and airmen and tarts and Black-market operators. He hadn't even drunk the beer he had ordered.

But he had paid for it. The coins lay on the counter. I drank the thin, ice-cold wartime lager for him, thinking: in a War you do see thousands of faces, some you get to know as well as your own, others are but a fleeting glimpse. It was odd how you ever remembered anybody; but you did. I wondered if I had, indeed, made a mistake. But the correct coins on the bar decided me.

It was him all right.

Marthaann Again

Marthaann turned up for Jane's funeral wearing a fox-fur, complete with realistic glass eyes. That fox had come to a curious end. Marthaann had run it down in her Ford Popular on a country road outside Alnwick, in Northumberland. It had, she reported, been transfixed in the headlights.

Inside three weeks it was around her neck.

'The woman,' said the Old Man, 'has all the sensitivity of Isaac Henderson, whom she much resembles.'

I could not remember my Grandfather Isaac, but Jane, the housekeeper, had imprinted him on my infant memory by constantly referring to him as if he were still alive, and by the various photographs around the old Newcastle house. Mostly, he was wearing Masonic Regalia, of which many of the vast mahogany dressers in the bedrooms were full. Sometimes I dressed up in the aprons and pinned the various starry medals on my shirt. Not when Jane was there. To her, his memory was sacred.

On the Fish Quay at North Shields the fishermen and fish-humpers would politely remark on my likeness to him, and were kind to me, in their rough way. Isaac's Foreman Boiler, Jimmy Nesbit, had once played Rugby Union for Northumberland, and would throw me a live crab, legs waving, to catch, as I stood staring into the bubbling, salty vats of water. I dropped the crab in, on his instructions. Jimmy heated the water slowly. He said it preserved the taste of the shellfish. You cannot do that now, by edict. It is thought to be cruel.

Jimmy was an oddity, a working-man in a cap and without teeth, although not yet forty, who played Rugby Union, a Gentleman's game. I often wondered how anybody had introduced him to it.

'You put me in mind of Isaac,' he told me. 'I hope you grow up a better paymaster.'

Marthaann inherited Jimmy and the other men when Isaac was killed, and faced down a lot of male prejudice on the Fish Quay. There were one or two other women to be seen buying stock for barrows or small shops, and, of course, hundreds of herring-girls moving with the Fisher-fleets in Season, and the famous Cullercoats Fish-wives with their shawls and long skirts and their Victorian poke-bonnets, the fish in wicker creels on their backs. All that was part of the scene.

But a woman bidding against men in the Fish Market? That was different.

Also, Marthaann was young, not more than thirty-two, bright and bonny and an armful. But with three children living and a couple dead, she could look the most intransigent male straight in the eye, be he Ship-owner or Auctioneer, until he became uncomfortably aware that he was dealing not with a mere woman but with somebody who knew all there was to know about shellfish and who could bid as well as any man and estimate profits as well as any man and who asked for no quarter because she was a woman.

After all, she had lived over the Shop all her life. She

had served in the Shop half of her life. And she was Isaac Henderson's daughter.

It was eventually enough.

Gradually, they accepted her, and no longer deliberately pushed her prices up when she bid for crabs, prawns and lobsters in the freezing, open sheds, slapping her tickets (with *I. V. Henderson* on them) onto the boxes and basses.

She never changed the Shop's name and was always addressed as 'Marthaann' (by her equals) and 'Missus Henderson' by her employees and inferiors. There was a very strict pecking-order on the Fish Quay.

So, she became Marthaann Henderson again, just as she had been before she married the Old Man, in the carefree moneyed days of her brief childhood and youth. Even her working day was like Isaac's.

Marthaann rose at six o'clock, dressed and drank a cup of hot tea and took the Electric Train from Heaton to North Shields. The train stopped at the bottom of the street, the reason Isaac had bought the house in the first place. She was on the Fish Quay before seven o'clock. The bidding and buying and supervising of the boiling of the stock occupied her until eleven o'clock, when she saw the stock on to the train at North Shields station, safely buried in salt and ice. No refrigeration then, and what a difference in the taste! Unless you have eaten prawns still warm after twenty minutes cooking in brine, you haven't eaten prawns. What you eat now is scampi, frozen and tasteless. Crabs do better, they have a stronger taste. But all food tasted stronger in those days, probably because some of it was going off, as the Old Man said.

Onkel Frank had once pronounced on a large male crab,

sent by Marthaann through the post. He sniffed it, and said, 'I should eat it today.'

None of us touched it!

Marthaann's day consisted of an uninterrupted six-hour morning, until she got back to the house at around noon. Jane, the housekeeper, had a meal for her, inevitably of fish, sometimes fried kippers or herrings or poached finny or boiled cod-roe; everything served with boiled potatoes. It had the advantage of being free. Nobody left the Fish Quay without a dainty morsel.

Meat, an enormous roast, was eaten on Sundays only, the Day of Rest. Marthaann found herself too tired for service at the Chapel, and did not go again regularly until she was in her seventies. She was finding that there were Other Things in life besides Hard Work and Prayer.

After an afternoon lie-down, Marthaann would get up, wash, and dress in her tailor-made suit. She was always a dresser, and watched wistfully by the out-of-work men on the street corners. A fine-looking woman, a *big* woman, was respected in those days.

Marthaann returned their looks, bade them Good Afternoon, and sailed on past them on her high heels, her fox-fur round her neck and cloche-hat firmly on her marcelled head. The men on the street corner sighed.

She was not for such as them.

Marthaann was a challenge to all men. She was a Career-woman before anybody invented them.

From three o'clock in the afternoon, she supervised and worked in her Shops, keeping a sharp eye on her girls for any slackness or sloppiness, exactly as Isaac had done. She closed down the Shops at eleven-thirty, caught the last tram, and was back in the house by midnight to eat her second meal of the day, usually a snack of some sort, with tea. She was in bed by one o'clock and up again at six.

Long hours but nobody thought much of it then.

Marthaann was well-off, making money, and free of any man.

Nobody envied her the last bit and maybe she didn't envy herself. But she didn't have a lot of time to dwell on it.

Except Sundays.

On Sundays, she and Peggy would roll up the carpet and Charleston wildly to the gramophone music, their short, Twenties' skirts riding high above their knees.

> 'When the Red, Red Robin comes Bob, Bob, Bobbin' along,
> Along,
> There'll be no more sobbin' when he starts singin'
> His old Sweet Song . . .'

Isaac frowned down at them from the wall as they danced faster than ever, two women in a room, only seventeen years between them.

On a Sunday, too.

And besides, all the men were dead in the War.

So what was the harm in it?

Nothing.

Just, somehow to me it felt sad.

Jane did most of the work, cooking and baking everything on a range in the kitchen. Sunday Dinner was eaten at about two o'clock and (like Isaac before her) Marthaann always had congenial company around her on these occasions. There would be Ted and Peg and myself, before we all went to Blackpool. Her sister-in-law, the Old Man's sister, Clara, who was on the Halls with her husband, Harold Carlisle, were guests when they were 'resting', which was increasingly often.

Their great days were behind them. But you would not have known it. They were everlastingly cheerful (or anyway, Clara was), telling stories of the Great Ones of the Halls, Lauder and Wilkie Bard (called that because he was always being 'Barred' for using Unsuitable Material) and George Lashwood, the Aristocratic Gentleman (who had started life as a mechanic) and Vesta Tilley, who really *was* a Lady and had married Sir Walter de Freece, the famous agent. These and many other names tripped off everybody's tongue as Marthaann was finally persuaded to sit down at the piano and play the famous, haunting songs of the old Music Hall.

> *'Are we to part like this, Bill?*
> *Are we to part this way?*
> *Who's it to be, 'er or me?*
> *You've only got to say . . .*
> *If it's all over between us,*
> *Don't ever pass me by.*
> *For you and me, still friends must be,*
> *For the sake of the days gone by . . .'*

Simple sentiments, but they touched the heart of all present, even my Uncle, the gloomy Scots Comic, Harold, so cynical by nature that he was the only Comic on the Halls to Go Off Without a Song!

'That, Son,' he told me, 'is begging the Punters. It's saying, Please Gimme Yer Kind Applause! I won't do it.'

'No, he won't,' said Clara. 'More fool him!'

Clara was boisterous, fun-loving, dark, vivacious and long-suffering, for Harold was not the easiest of husbands. Nobody was, then. He finally blotted his copy-book, as they used to say, when standing at the Stage-door in the West End during the Interval, having his pipe, No Smoking being allowed in Artistes' Dressing Rooms. He was greeted by Scotch football-supporters down for the International. They produced a bottle and he drank deeply from it, and went down the road to the Pub with them. He did not go back for the Second House, the most heinous crime in the Book, and never worked on the Big Circuits again. What melancholy had led him to do such a thing was never known.

Even Clara, who sang so cheerfully alongside Marthaann, could not cajole him from his misery. Like all comics, he was by nature gloomy. Even his jokes had a mournful note: 'The weather's so changeable, you don't know what to pawn.'

'The little man is good, therefore always in work at some level,' said the Old Man. 'However, he is personally Bad Company.'

They got on, both being married to extrovert and high-spirited women, not given to introspection at any time, and noisy with it.

'Marthaann and Clara, the two of them together,' said the Old Man, 'would give a hippo the headache.'

Certainly, they equated enjoyment with hilarity. Marthaann, who could pay any tune by ear if she heard it once, plonking on the piano and Clara singing the verse, and everybody else joining in with the chorus of *Nellie Dean* or *In The Twi-Twi-Twilight*.

Jane was part of it, in her long white apron over her black bombazine skirt, her white hair combed back, working quietly and laughing as Marthaann slapped my sister Peggy for imitating Clara's throaty, false chorus-girl's voice and never missing a beat as she did so.

★

Jane was always there. Always had been, all my young life, a fixture.

And now she was dead, not in her beloved Newcastle but in a tawdry place like Blackpool, which I had heard her call the Last Place God Made. She died suddenly, in bed, quietly, without fuss, as she had lived her life.

It was the first time anybody close to me had died. In those days people did not show their feelings as they do now. It was unthinkable for a young man to cry. You were expected to take it all in your stride, as they used to say. Jane had really been a mother to me, since Marthaann was always busy at her Shops. She had been a mother to us all, and now she was gone. It was a bleak, wordless time. I was now in my last year at school, the summer holidays would be my last freedom, and now this. I was devastated.

The Old Man seemed to be the only one with any idea of the depth of my loss. I was in my mid-teens and almost a man, so there was a limit to what he could say. However, he recalled funerals of old and made remarks about them to take the sting out of the one we were all preparing for.

'The thing we must do,' he said, 'is to have plenty of ham. People expect ham. And tongue. Plenty of tongue. And drink. Lots of drink. That's the thing.'

The house was suddenly full of flowers.

Everybody was coming.

My sister Peggy and her new husband Matt, a Catholic Minor-public-schoolboy, who had played wing-three-quarter for the County and was a bit of a hero to me. He good-naturedly supported General Franco in Spain, against the assaults of the family. He was respected on account of it. He also liked a bet, which meant the Old Man took him under his wing. Matt was an even worse judge of a horse than the Old Man was.

Ted was there, of course, and Clara and Uncle Harold were coming on the day, as they were working in Variety at Bolton and could get across in the morning and back by train for the first house. There were many neighbours, such as Jack's parents, Harold and Sannah. The front door was left open to admit them, for a drink and a sandwich, after or before the carriages. It was all very cheerful and the house seemed strange. I wondered what we would all do without Jane. For one thing, there would be no smell of newly-baked bread filling the house. It was all very disorientating, made all the more so by a decision I had to make, and at once.

I was offered an Arts scholarship.

The Art Master had fixed it for me. I drew well but could not paint with any real talent, and that worried me. I took the Old Man along to see the Manager of the Printing Department at the local paper, who also ran an Art and Graphics department, printing Christmas cards and Birthday cards, and were prosperous, successful and well-regarded. I told the Old Man that the Manager had seen samples of my work and liked them and it seemed he'd take me on. It was a working apprenticeship. I'd work in the Print Shop part-time and go to the local Art School part-time.

In those days few people went on to University, and although it had been obvious to at least one teacher that I was 'University material', nothing was done about it. Years later I met that teacher in the street. I said I had already written two novels and some radio plays, and lived to hear the answer, 'Yes, but you *were* University material, you know!'

Teachers never leave school.

Nor, for that matter, do professors.

Anyway, in those days writers were expected to knock around the world a bit, to do a variety of exciting jobs and to go to Wars. All this was thought to give an author something to write about, as well as a knowledge of men and affairs.

I suppose my generation was the last of that lot.

I didn't take the Art Scholarship.

The Old Man, since there was no pay, thought it was perhaps a way of getting cheap labour in a hard and difficult decade. But I think it was the rough Lancashire accent of the Printing Manager that decided him against it. The Printing Manager was an NCO type. I suspect the Old Man thought he might be a bullying employer. There were a lot of them around then. The world was a much rougher place. The Manager told me I'd start by washing brushes and I could not expect to be let loose on original drawing of any sort for a very long time. Since I thought I could draw pretty well already, that was a blow. I think it was kindly meant; the Manager didn't want me to think it was an easy job. He'd had to work unspeakably long hours to get where he was and he didn't want me to think it would be a walk-over.

Part of the problem was that I was fairly good-looking and quick with words and, I suppose, by the standards of the Print Shop, a bit above myself. I wasn't really, but in Lancashire they are on the look-out for any of that. It is Nonconformist country.

I hadn't liked the thumping noise of the Press and I doubted somehow if I'd ever be allowed to draw anything decent in such a place.

'I don't think so,' I told the Old Man.

'I agree, not for you.'

But what was?

And the Art Master was not pleased when I told him. I was sorry. He'd gone to trouble he didn't need to.

I felt bad about it and resolved to get the first suitable job I could. I had no idea what I was up against.

In the weeks before Jane's death, I had written to six or seven office jobs advertised in the local paper without getting a reply, and I was beginning to worry. After all, I was top in just about everything. What more was required to get a measly office job?

Luck was required.

I had it when I decided to apply for a job in person. I went on my bike, telling nobody, not even the Old Man, who was debating asking Edwards to pay my way through College – and I didn't want *that*. I could imagine Aunt Dorothy's Frosty Face!

My prospective employer, Mister Henny, was called Leonard behind his back and 'Mister Henny' to his face, by his staff of fifteen. He was a factor or wholesaler and sold every kind of radio and electrical spare-part, plus cycles and radiograms and all sorts of other unlikely items that even his warehousemen knew nothing about. He was a fair-haired, slightly chubby man in his thirties, and I learned a lot from him. He was an excellent businessman in a hard time for businessmen or indeed anybody else. He profoundly dis-agreed with my half-baked Socialism and I used to argue with him so passionately about politics that Joe, the Chief Warehouseman, had to take me aside and whisper, 'Stop arguing wi' Leonard, lad, or he'll bloody sack thee!'

It was to Leonard's credit he didn't.

'I've been to Germany. There's nobody standing about on the street corners there,' he'd say.

'No,' I'd reply, 'they are all in prison, those that don't agree with Hitler.'

Joe, the Warehouseman, told me I didn't know what I was talking about.

What I did know was that I had spilt a bottle of ink all over Leonard's splendid desk while I was applying for the job, and he just sat there looking at me, waiting to see what I would do next.

I picked up an old-fashioned blotter and blotted up the ink and kept talking.

He gave me the job.

Before he did that, he went to see the Old Man. When I saw his car outside the house my heart sank – what impression would the Old Man make on him? I went to my friend Jack's house until I was sure he'd gone.

When I went into the house, the Old Man seemed unperturbed. 'Couldn't work for a more pleasant fellow,' he said. 'I'd say he was a White Man.'

Leonard too had succumbed to the Old Man's charm. 'What is the country coming to when a splendid fellow like your father is having problems finding a job, when hundreds of men like him gave their lives, or anyway their youth, in the trenches, and he can't find a decent job? The country owes him that, at least!'

I was tempted to say the Old Man owed the country (or anyway several of its citizens) a lot, too, but I didn't.

After all, I had the job.

Fifty-four other boys, all from local grammar-schools and with excellent School Certificate passes, had applied for my job, in excellent hands (copperplate, some of them, I'd seen their letters, found I actually knew several of them), and failed to get the job because I had it.

Fifty-five of us and I'd got it.

It was either luck or the Old Man's charm.

Probably, I thought, a bit of both.

Onkel Frank turned up at Jane's funeral in an unconventional way, even for him.

The house had a narrow entry on one side, known in Lancashire as a ginnel. We didn't use it, as it was very narrow and led only to a locked and barred back door, six feet high, which in turn led on to the yard.

Onkel Frank entered by that door, despite the fact that the front door of the house was open.

'Has the man finally taken leave of his senses?' hissed the Old Man between his teeth, as he saw, through the window of the kitchen, a highly polished shoe first appear above the door.

'Who is it?' I asked.

'Who do you think?'

The next item on view was a hat.

By this time the neighbours and guests were all over the ground floor of the house. Those in the kitchen, amongst them Marthaann, stopped whatever they were doing, curiosity roused by the noise of Onkel Frank's shoes rap-tapping up to the door and finally ending with him perched on top of the door, lighted cigarette in mouth.

'Is that Frank?' enquired Marthaann, a superfluous question. Who else would enter a house by a barred back door when the front door was open?

For a moment Onkel Frank remained poised on the top of the door and then he sprang down, landing in the yard with some aplomb. He was much the fittest of the brothers, as he walked everywhere, disliking the confinement of trams and taxis. It was of a piece with his fear of thunder.

Nowadays such behaviour might be understood and even sympathised with. Not then.

'Your Uncle Frank,' said Marthaann, 'is as daft as ever, I see.'

Behaviour always rated highly with Marthaann.

Like all Nonconformists, she had a sharp eye for the failings of others.

'He's all right,' I said. He had taken me on literally hundreds of walks in the park when I was a very small boy, talking to me as if I was an adult, telling me stories. I owed my love of history and literature to him.

The Old Man opened the kitchen door and admitted Onkel Frank. 'Why,' he asked quietly, as everybody stared, 'didn't you come in the fokkin front door like everybody else?'

He did not seem to expect an answer.

It was as well for he didn't get one.

Onkel Frank accepted a glass of whisky from the Old Man.

Before it had reached his lips, Marthaann spoke. 'Frank,' she said. 'A little bit of respect? A black tie?

Onkel Frank moved forward until he was eyeballing her at a four-inch distance. She did not flinch.

'Black tie?' Onkel Frank said. 'I can't afford Black *Food*!'

And passed on into the other room.

Said Marthaann. 'They don't call him Barmy for nothing. Percy, I blame you!'

'Why,' asked the Old Man mildly, 'is that?'

'You know what he's like. You shouldn't have invited him.'

'I didn't invite him. He's free to come and go as he pleases. As you are.'

'Taking the easy way out, as usual,' said Marthaann.

'Not always,' responded the Old Man. 'I married you. I wouldn't call that the easy way out.'

'A forced push is no choice,' retorted Marthaann.

'Just the same,' said the Old Man, 'some people might not have, you know.'

Marthaann stared at him, her eyes bright with anger.

I said, 'Did you notice anything odd about Onkel Frank?'

'Apart from he kept his hat on in this house all the time?' said Marthaann, promptly. 'A disgrace, I call that! And he kept his raincoat on!'

'He has no jacket or waistcoat under it, that's why,' I said.

The Old Man looked interested, and went out of the room.

Marthaann said, 'Do you want to come back to Newcastle with me? You can go to school there, as long as you like.'

'I've got a job,' I said. 'I start next week. In an office.'

'Do you want that? Where will it lead to?'

'I don't know. The Boss seems a nice man.'

'I have the Shops. Peggy doesn't want them. Or Ted. He thinks it's beneath him, they both do, selling shellfish.'

'You'll be running them yourself for a long time yet.'

Marthaann nodded. 'Yes, I will, but somebody has to have them. Are you interested?'

I shook my head. 'I'd be useless in that trade. You have to learn it, like you and grandfather did, from the floor up.'

Marthaann nodded grimly, hurt. 'Too educated for it? I see! But there's money in it, young fella, and who else in the Family except Edwards and me have got any money? Has your Uncle Frank?'

I said, 'There are only two meetings a week at the Track. So he's not doing so well.'

'Gave up his handicapping job in Barnsley, I hear.'

'Well, he did, yes, but that was because they wanted him to handicap the Dogs unfairly so they would get a lot of money out of it. He wouldn't do it.'

Marthaann wasn't surprised. 'You have no room for that sort of behaviour if you have a wife and three children to feed.'

'You wouldn't expect him to do that?'

'Well, he didn't and now he's here in Blackpool and from what he says, he's badly off.'

'I think he exaggerated when he said he hadn't any food.'

'Frank always exaggerates. About everything.' Marthaann shook her head. 'I've seen him add up figures in the air with his fingers, and when his sums were wrong, wet his finger and rub them out! Rub out figures in the air that weren't there in the first place!'

'Well,' I said, 'he's different.'

'Different enough so he didn't get married until he was fifty. And where's Florrie?'

'I expect she'll turn up,' I said, edging away.

'So you're not coming back?' she said.

'I have the job, you see?'

Marthaann nodded. 'Oh, yes. I see.'

She took offence faster than anybody except Onkel Frank. Which was why they rarely spoke to each other. It could so quickly turn into a row.

The Old Man hove back into the room. 'You were right. He has no jacket or waistcoat on.'

'Why, did he say?'

'Apparently,' said the Old Man, 'Florrie didn't want him to come to the funeral.'

'Why?'

Said the Old Man, irritably, 'How do I know?'

I tried to puzzle it out.

'She kept his coat and waistcoat?'

'It seems so.'

'But why do a thing like that?'

'There are some things in this world,' the Old Man said, 'that are known only to God, and sometimes not even to Him.'

And with that I had to be content.

I didn't go to the funeral. I couldn't face it.

I went to my friend Jack's and we played table-football. I felt terrible. I felt terrible all that week and all the next week.

And then I went to work for Mr Henny.

In the hurly-burly of my new life, telephones ringing, invoices to write, with the warehousemen shouting orders in my ear, cycling furiously to work and furiously home, dog-tired at the end of each day, doing a man's work for a youth's pay, I had joined the vast freemasonry of work. It blotted out everything else. It even blotted out my sorrow.

I didn't think of Jane again, not for many, many months. And then it didn't hurt so much. It was still sorrow but it was a hurtful, distant sorrow that belonged to my childhood.

And I had put away childish things.

On the Knocker

The Old Man had two boasts.

The first, that he had never taken money from a woman.

The second, that he had never been reduced to selling those Bloody Vacuums. He meant Vacuum Cleaners. And he meant door-to-door, or, more properly, On the Knocker.

In the late Thirties, everybody who was out of work, strapped for money or needed stamps for their cards, found themselves, sooner or later, On the Knocker. Below a minimum of stamps they would receive No Dole.

Firms who employed door-to-door salesmen normally paid thirty bob a week, plus travel expenses (if necessary) plus commission. But they also stamped your cards, weekly. Which kept you on Ordinary Unemployment Benefit. Which kept you out of the hands of the Means Test Inspectors, who were the most feared men, bar nobody, in the country.

Young men who had a job were forced to leave home because their wages were counted-in against the total family-budget, which was something like subsistence-level for most unemployed men. Women who worked were rare but if they did that was counted-in, too. The Old Man – who, as my sister Peggy remarked, was a Socialist when he had nothing, but a Tory when he had – was indignant about such treatment of the Ordinary Man.

He was right, of course. But he found himself On the Knocker one day. Not exactly knocking at doors, no, but close.

The Dogs were down to one meeting a week and pickings were small. The winters were the worst, as they were for everybody in Blackpool, who existed through the winter on the fat of summer profits from the Visitors, like some hibernating animal.

Even Edwards the Bookie had it hard in winter. Punters didn't bet over the Jumps.

They should, said Onkel Frank. If you back a Favourite and a Second Favourite for a Place, in a small field, over the Season you must show a profit. It was about the only likely system he knew but Bookies, if you persist in it, would and will Put the Bar Up, that is, refuse to accept your bets. By law, they are within their rights. Like a publican refusing you a drink.

It was a System that was no use to the Old Man, who was always looking, as Onkel Frank said, for One to Beat the Favourite. That way, you get poor fast.

So, the middle of November of that year found the Old Man having to seriously consider employment. It was a drastic decision, but, as he said, needs must.

Even Edwards was no help.

Onkel Frank spoke the last word. 'He's holed up waiting for summer, like some old grey rat.'

Onkel Frank never even considered an ordinary job because he could always get handicapping posts here and there.

Ted, my brother, was working for Edwards in his office. Remuneration, two pounds a week. Ted was dressy, or as dressy as you can be on two suits, three shirts and a pair of spats. He was taking out a girl. The two pounds didn't go very far. The Old Man understood that. Ted kept threatening to leave his Uncle's employment, but where was another job to be found? Nobody wanted a young, qualified engineering draughtsman.

The Old Man, without seeming difficulty, landed a job selling Tonic Wine. The liquid was called *Wintonic* and was mostly alcohol. So the old ladies who bought it at the door naturally felt better when they drank some.

The Old Man was to be the Manager of a 'Team' of salesmen, some dozen strong, working the small towns of the North of England. Amongst other things, he had to decide which streets to try first. Suburban streets with gardens were best. Terraced-houses, forget them. There was no training in sales-technique, or anything like that, just an hour's chat in a shabby office in Manchester and then they were On the Road in two battered old vans full of crates of *Wintonic*.

Destination: the North East.

As the Old Man said, trying to sell Tonic Wine in an officially designated Depressed Area was 'the act of a madman'.

The price of the bottles: two shillings and elevenpence; two-and-three if you bought a crate of six.

The Team consisted of unemployed men, mostly young, who had done this sort of thing before. They wore shabby suits, shoes that often took in water, and they had been On the Knocker before, trying to get householders to change their daily newspaper, trying to sell hand-lotion, hair-lotion, tubes of magic pain-cure, shoes, sewing-machines, socks; you name it, they had tried to sell it. Almost all had descended at some time or other to the hardest sell of all, the Vacuum

Cleaner, so hated (in prospect) by the Old Man. This was because anybody selling them had to lug them around the streets by hand and, even worse, fanny-up housewives by doing 'a Demo': that is, vacuuming a room or hallway. This the Old Man considered a demeaning task for a man, reducing him to some kind of servant. He wondered how anybody could do it. Some of his redoubtable Team had the answer. Very easily. The trick was to make love to the housewife before the sales-pitch. Not necessarily on the first visit, but soon. Because Teams On the Knocker were out of town as soon as possible.

The Old Man knew that few of his Team would go that far to sell a bottle or two of *Wintonic*.

Not that they sold many bottles.

The needy citizens of Stockton-on-Tees, Whitby, Scarborough and suchlike were finding it hard to satisfy their appetites for their meagre dinners, without the promised appetite-restoring qualities of the Tonic Wine. A few dozen bottles a day – never, ever a crate – was the average, and the Old Man could see that even his Team's miserable thirty-bob wages were not being covered by sales, or anything like it. The Team found it hard enough to survive on the thirty bob. They stayed a week in each town, paying six shillings each for a shared Combined Room. Usually two men would bunk together, often in the same bed. Nobody thought that unusual then.

In these Combined Rooms there was usually a gas-ring attached to a meter. On these the Team fried sausages and boiled potatoes. Otherwise it was tea, bread and marge, for all meals. Add a few packets of cigarettes, and the need to send at least a pound a week home to the wife and kids, this meant absolute penury, most of the time.

The wages-money came through on Friday mornings by car from Head Office. Thirty bob plus commission. The problem being there was no commission, or very little.

The Old Man lived in a boarding-house with breakfast and an evening meal provided, but he was getting four pounds a week. He found that he unofficially 'subbed' the neediest of his team to a sum total of about a pound a week. He was accordingly popular.

Out of desperation and boredom, he decided to do some selling himself. Nowadays, they would call it leading from the front.

He had no more luck than anybody else, despite his selection of Dixon, his best salesman, as a partner. Dixon, he recalled later, was the finest door-to-door salesman he'd ever met. 'The man could sell anything to anybody. Napoleon always asked of a Captain up for promotion, "Is he lucky?" '

Dixon was lucky.

Example: the Old Man and Dixon approached two workmen's cottages in the village of Consett, County Durham. Consett had just about the highest rate of unemployment in the United Kingdom. Nobody had sold a single bottle of *Wintonic* in the first four days.

The Old Man and Dixon walked to the two cottages through deep, freezing snow. It was the week before Christmas.

'Which house do you want?' asked the Old Man.

Dixon said, 'The one on the left.'

The Old Man hit the knocker on his door, Dixon the same on his.

An elderly man in grey-looking long-johns answered the Old Man's door. He was holding a candle against the gloom because the electric had been switched off for non-payment.

He was in bed to keep warm, having run out of coal, despite living in the middle of a huge coalfield.

He informed the Old Man that, far from being in the market for a bottle of *Wintonic*, he did not have the porridge for his breakfast. On discovering he was an Old Soldier, the Old Man gave him a florin.

Dixon, next door, sold a crate of six bottles of *Wintonic* to two old maiden-ladies, who took him in, gave him tea and buns, and paid cash.

The Old Man said, 'You cannot allow for that kind of luck. Dixon had it. Simple as that.'

Dixon's sale to the two maiden-ladies was to be the only good news that week. The bad news was that the wages didn't arrive.

Friday went by and Friday night went by and Saturday morning came, and still no car with the wages. The Team thought the firm had gone bust.

The Old Man rang the office but got no reply. It snowed and snowed.

Christmas Day was on the Sunday. The Old Man told the Team the wages were held up. The Team couldn't go anywhere without money.

Dixon approached the Old Man on behalf of them all. 'Percy, these lads are in a mess. If they don't get paid, how will they get home for Christmas?'

The Old Man thought long on that, smoking a whole Churchman's while doing it. Then he told Dixon to load every crate of *Wintonic* they had into one of the old vans. They drove to the biggest Pawnbroker in Consett. Pawnbrokers were just about the only people doing any good in the Depression, anyway in the Depressed Areas. The Old Man told the Pawnbroker a version of the truth. That the wages hadn't come through and he needed enough on the wine to cover the train-fares home. That was, he reckoned, about a pound a man. Ten pounds. He'd redeem the wine on New Year's Day.

The Pawnbroker demurred.

The Old Man pointed to the price on the labels and the number of bottles. 'There's two hundred pounds' worth of wine here!'

The Pawnbroker gave in. The Old Man left him looking bemused.

The Old Man came out of the Pawnshop and gave every man his train-fare home. He couldn't give them their wages because he hadn't got them. And it was Christmas Eve. He sent a sixpenny telegram to the firm telling them that their vans (empty) were parked in the main street, the keys with the two maiden-ladies. He reminded them they owed wages to everybody, including himself.

He never heard from the firm. They had gone broke and done a Flit.

His final comment was, 'I hope that Pawnbroker likes Tonic Wine.'

People in the Thirties were forever casting around for an idea that could get you rich quick.

Probably, as the Old Man said, 'because there is no such animal'.

When I asked him what he meant, he said, 'There was a cartoon in *Punch* about a hundred years ago. It showed a man looking at a giraffe. Now, in those times nobody had ever seen a giraffe. So the man says, "There's no such animal!" Well, there's no such animal as a get-rich-quick idea.'

'Inventions?' I said. 'Edison's electric bulb?'

'Nothing much left to discover, I'd say. Besides, you're talking Science and they're talking Money.'

'Are you saying there are no new ideas?'

'Damn few, now.'

'How about Books on Wheels? That's a new idea, isn't it?'

The Old Man shook his head. He had doubts if it was a get-rich-quick idea. It was an On-the-Knocker idea, and therefore couldn't be.

Books on Wheels was an invention of the Yorkshire writer William Holt, known in the family as Willy. Willy Holt was a tackler or overseer at a mill in Todmorden, who saw there was more to life than that. So he wrote a book, called *Under a Japanese Parasol*, which had nothing to do with Japan. This brought him into contact with Publishers, because one of them printed his book. Soon, he was printing and selling them himself. After that, he thought about Readers, and worked out that if you could bring the books to their door, you had a get-rich-quick idea.

Well, not exactly get-rich-quick because Willy Holt was a Communist and he probably didn't care about the money. Those working for him did, devoutly. They included my sister Peggy's husband, Matt, the Rugby player. He was Northern Manager of Books on Wheels and Willy Holt was General Manager. Matt was sure it was a get-rich-quick idea. Meantime, he worked ninety-hours-a-week for four pounds.

Willy Holt was the first author I ever saw. He ran to a dark, double-breasted overcoat, a bowler hat and highly polished boots. He was in Blackpool to see my brother Ted, who was working for Books on Wheels in the town.

Books on Wheels worked this way. You rented a book at the door for twopence. You had it for a week. You selected it from the books on the van.

Here was the difference. You could get a book at the Public Library for nothing. But you had to go out for it, make a special journey for it. With Books on Wheels you didn't.

Ted, or somebody like him, knocked on your door. It was an On-the-Knocker Job but genteel with it.

The van, as Matt explained it to the family, was a marvel. 'Willy Holt got the manufacturer to build him one on spec, because he had no money, and he drove it across the Pennines to Manchester himself, in thunder and lightning, to demonstrate it to his backers. It was so good, they gave him the money to buy a dozen.'

That was big money. The sponsors were Quakers.

'Willy Holt,' said the Old Man, 'didn't mind joining in the prayers they then said for a successful enterprise. He'd have joined in if they'd been Fuzzy Wuzzies.'

The vans were long, like an old steam train in design, with the shelves (which were shuttered) at the front. The driver sat at the back in a compartment not unlike that of a steam-train driver. It was powered by a motor-cycle engine. The vans were a bit heavy to handle and one that Ted was driving capsized and took fire. Ted ran into a nearby house and got a pail of water or six and put the fire out. The local paper reported it and Ted was a sort of hero.

Willy Holt seemed less impressed. He was a blunt York-shireman and he was not quick with praise for Ted's action. Ted, with brilliantined hair and a leather coat and brown brogues, was a bit upmarket (as they say now) for Willy Holt.

'I put the fire out,' Ted said. 'What did I do wrong?'

'Let it burn,' suggested the Old Man, 'and let them collect the Insurance?'

Nobody else had thought of that.

Anyway, the job went on for a bit, but there was no real money in it, On the Knocker. A plus (as they say now) was that the front room of the house was full of books, mostly novels. All kinds of novels: crime, literary, everything. I bean-feasted on those books. I read Lawrence's *Seven Pillars of Wisdom* before the customers did. I read Linklater and Priestley and Cronin and Howard Spring before the customers did. I read on average one book a night before I went to bed, boggle-eyed at two or three o'clock. Nobody objected.

The Old Man simply said, 'I don't know how you do it,' his stock reaction to most things I did.

When Ted lost the job the books stayed in the front room, nobody seemed to know why. The Books on Wheels experiment went on elsewhere, and Matt went on working his socks off to make a success of it all. And then the War came and put a stop to it, and Matt went into the Fire Service.

But not yet.

Before that, Ted was fired with a get-rich-quick idea himself. Again, it was an On-the-Knocker idea.

This time it wasn't Books or *Wintonic*.

It was Cocoa-Whisk.

In a way, it was Ted's answer to Matt's previous On-the-Knocker effort. This was the Matzo Crackers idea. Matt had bought three vans from a firm who made Matzo Crackers for the Jewish population of the big cities of the North. These vans were full of Matzo biscuits, which are thin, crackly, and a bit of an acquired taste. Matt repacked them and got a Team of canvassers, many of them Jewish, to come along, as it were, with the van and the Matzos.

These were redoubtable canvassers and wondrous men On the Knocker. But all their efforts failed. Even their valiant description of the Matzos as Chocolate Wheaten or Custard Creams failed to gain a response. They could do this with safety because the Matzos were wrapped so tightly in cellophane it was impossible to open them inside five minutes. In which time the Team was out of the street.

They sold few packets. As the Old Man said, 'I wonder what them as bought them made of them!'

Also, the vans broke down. So even that super optimist, Matt, had to call it a day and go and work for Willy Holt.

Ted thought he could go one better. He hired a room in Preston and installed in it two young girls. They filled packets marked *Van Dyke Food Products, London, Birmingham and Manchester* (but no address) with a mixture of cocoa and chemist's chalk. The chalk was added to give the packets weight. Ted then hired a Team and their pitch to the bewildered housewives was 'Cocoa-Whisk, the Health Drink, one-and-three a packet, Two for the Price of One!'

I think they sold about twenty packets in a week. It was a bigger disaster than the Matzos.

The Old Man spoke for everybody that Christmas when he said, standing with his back to the fireplace, whisky glass in hand, 'That On-the-Knocker game is no good to anybody, man nor beast.'

The War was looming ever nearer now. People said there would be Food Rationing.

Declared the Old Man, 'We'll never starve in this house. We have enough Cocoa-Whisk and Matzo Crackers and Books to last us for ten years!'

And that was all anybody ever got out of the Knocker.

'The Biggest Rat in the World'

I shook hands with the Rector of Stiffkey.

He was in a barrel on the Golden Mile.

Truth to tell, I was disappointed. I had expected him to be peeping over the top of the large water-butt, possibly half-filled with water, the better to cleanse away his sins of the flesh. Which, according to the *News of the World*, were many. For the Rector was possibly the most famous man in England that summer, having been recently defrocked for indulging in sexual practices with loose women, in that Bed of Vice, Soho. He was said to have prayed with them.

'Before or after?' the Old Man had asked, of nobody in particular.

'How de do?' The Rector extended a firm hand, which I took. He was certainly in a barrel, as advertised, but it had been engineered to look like a throne, and he simply sat on it and greeted the punters, who were queuing four-deep along the Prom, with a cheery word. 'God bless you,' he intoned, and the audience was over.

The Rector looked anything but bored. His life had taken a turn he could never have expected. To be exhibited at sixpence a time to the mill-workers of Lancashire and Yorkshire, on the most famous stretch of sea-front in the world, should surely have shaken him into a permanent sense of wonder at the workings of the Lord.

Apparently not. He seemed to be indifferent to his fame. Within a year he was to be eaten by a lion at a circus in Germany. Of course, none of us knew that yet.

The Old Man was still outside talking to Luke Gannon.

Luke Gannon was the foremost impresario of the Golden Mile, which stretched (it still does) from the Tower to the Central Pier, for exactly that length, but is now covered in a rash of video games and fruit-machine arcades. Then it was full of Sideshows and Song Booths and still had a fairground air about it. The song of that summer was *Red Sails in the Sunset* and I could hear it drifting along the Mile, above the cries of the rock-sellers and the pitch-men trying to get the punters into the salesrooms to buy mirrors and lampshades and canteens of cutlery and dresses and all sorts of gear (the Showman's word) they would never have dreamed of buying on a wet Saturday afternoon in Burnley or Bolton.

But here in Blackpool, the sun was shining and it was another world of wonder and delight. The trippers wore paper hats and were many of them drunk, either with the strong bitter served in the hundred pubs of the town, or with the sheer intoxication of simply being in Blackpool.

The Mile was the place to have a stall or a show if you wanted to make money, and who didn't want to do that in 1938?

Luke Gannon certainly did, but he had been making money on the Mile for half a century, so none of this was new. He was modest to those who said that putting the Rector of Stiffkey in a barrel was a brainwave. 'It just seemed to fit,' he was explaining to the Old Man. 'Now, with Sacko, that was different. People had to feel afraid for him, afraid he wouldn't last out the night, y'see?'

Sacko the Fasting Man had been at the Mile the previous summer. He had broken all records for attendances. He held the world record for fasting, over sixty days, made in his native Italy some years before. I had seen him on the Mile and he looked thin and ill to death, sitting in his chair in a sort of mocked-up cave. People had filed past him in wonder, not speaking or even whispering. He had seemed a much more religious figure than the Rector of Stiffkey.

Of course, Cyril, my friend Jack's mentor at the Co-operative Butchery Department, insisted that Sacko had returned to his digs in Palatine Road, there to enjoy a nightly pint of Guinness and a pork pie at the end of a long day's fasting.

True or false it didn't matter.

People believed he was fasting because they wanted to believe it. It was of a piece with their belief in Tom Thumb and the Siamese Twins. It was the element of wonder that did it. According to Luke Gannon.

He was a big man in a hat, smoking a cigar. He said, 'Percy, there's money on the Mile but you have to have something people want to see.' He looked at the ash on his cigar. 'Do you have that?'

The Old Man was pensive. 'Just asking, Luke.'

Luke Gannon looked disbelieving. 'If you have any ideas, I'm always open for business.' And he nodded and went across to the kiosk to count the takings.

The Old Man was unusually silent, sitting on the tram, going south along the Prom. I said, 'What did Mr Gannon mean, any idea?'

'Just something I'd been thinking about,' said the Old Man. Behind us, the sound of the song booths faded and then the subdued roar of the crowds on the Mile. The Old Man was obviously thinking hard about something but, whatever it was, he was keeping it to himself.

The next evening he sent me to see Harry Budd to borrow his employer's car for an hour or two.

'Where do I tell him we're going?'

'Say out to Marton Moss, and we'll be about an hour all told.'

It took us almost that long to find the farm. Well, it wasn't exactly a farm, more a run-down smallholding out on the Moss, and it was full of animals in cages. Rabbits, ferrets, dogs (greyhounds and whippets mostly) and cats, all kinds of furry creatures, even some that looked suspiciously like foxes. The Old Man didn't seem to notice the smell. He loved all animals, having kept so many of them as a boy. He peered at the animals and made friendly noises to them. Harry Budd had parked the car at the gate and was pointedly looking at his pocket-watch.

'What are we doing here?' I asked.

But the Old Man was looking past me. 'Alf!'

I turned round. A lean and mournful man in dirty overalls and clogs was standing watching us, a pail of animal food in his hand. He was unshaven and spoke in the country dialect.

'Nah then, Percy, how arta?'

'Very fair, Alf. This is my son. This is Alf, the Animal Man.'

I had seen Alf the Animal Man before. He was a Donkey-ride Man, amongst other things, and trooped his animals down to the Sands whenever the tide was out and the visitors in. He was famous, in a small way, for being able to obtain any bird or animal you might want to buy, or find an owner for one you wanted to sell, such transactions always carrying a commission for himself. He was reputed to know all there was to know about animals or birds, their illnesses, their weaknesses, and the cures thereof. Almost everybody in Blackpool knew somebody who had had dealings with him.

He was looking at the Old Man in a shrewd and calculating way that I wasn't sure I liked. After all, he was a Moss-ite, a peasant who had been living all his life in that stretch of watery farmland behind the great coastal resort, where nothing had changed since the Dutch engineers had drained Marton Mere and built the vast network of dykes two hundred years before. Moss-ites didn't like the townspeople. They wore clogs and spoke their own patois and kept themselves to themselves.

'Doesta want the lad in this?'

The Old Man looked surprised at the question. 'Why not?'

The Animal Man shrugged. 'It's up to thee. So long as he knows enough to keep his lips together.' He put down the food bucket and took a bunch of keys from his pocket. Wordlessly, he trudged across the clarty farmyard towards a low wooden building standing apart from the others. He unlocked the heavy door and pulled it open. A pungent smell met our nostrils, stronger than anything we had smelled so far, which was saying something.

The Animal Man went into the place and lit an oil-lamp. 'Come on in and shut t'door behind thee.'

We went inside. It was dark after the evening sunshine.

Then we saw the Rat. It was housed in a large cage of wire and wood, and it was not moving, just sitting there, a huge bundle of fur and eyes and teeth, staring at us, or, more probably, at the light.

The Old Man drew in his breath sharply. 'That's a hell of a Rat, Alf.'

'It is,' said the Animal Man. 'It's the Biggest Rat in the World, is that.'

The Old Man shook his head. 'I've never seen anything as big as that, ever.'

Said Alf, 'Thou won't neither, even if thou lives to be a hundred.'

'It must be a foreign beast?' said the Old Man.

'I can't tell thee where it comes frae,' said the Animal Man, 'but it isn't frae hereabouts. I had to pay a pretty penny for it, tha knows.'

The Old Man pondered long but said no more.

In the half-dark the Rat made a squealing sound. I wished we could get out of the place. The smell was terrible. I felt sick with it.

The Old Man lit a cigarette against it.

Alf the Animal Man blew his nose with his fingers. I felt even sicker.

The Old Man must have noticed something because he said, 'I think we can talk outside, Alf.'

Outside, I went across to Harry Budd at the car.

'What's in that shed?' asked Harry Budd, who wasn't, as they said, born yesterday.

'I can't say,' I said.

Harry Budd nodded and looked at his watch again. 'I knew a fella who bought a dog off Alf,' he said. 'It weren't what he said it were.'

I didn't reply. I was watching the Old Man and Alf. They were standing in the farmyard smoking and talking in a serious fashion. Finally, the Old Man shook hands with Alf and came towards us. He looked pleased with himself but said nothing all the way back to the town.

All the way I could hear in my head the mournful keening sounds of the caged animals, dogs and cats and foxes and I couldn't seem to get the smell of them out of my nostrils.

When we were safely back in the house, the Old Man finally spoke.

'The Biggest Rat in the World!' He sipped his whisky. 'It takes some thinking about, doesn't it?'

'In what way?' I asked, uneasily.

'All will be revealed in good time,' said the Old Man, switching on Late Night Dance Music by Henry Hall and his Orchestra.

Well, it beat the desperate howls of the animals.

Onkel Frank was not impressed by the Old Man's proposition. They were sitting in the front room smoking cigarettes and talking in low voices but I heard enough to follow the gist of it.

'A Giant Rat?' Onkel Frank was asking.

'Exactly,' said the Old Man.

'You think people will pay to see a Giant Rat?'

'Sure of it.'

'Why should they do that?'

'Because most people have seen a rat or two in their lives. This one is six times the size of any rat you've ever seen. Or I've ever seen, and I saw some beauties in the Trenches.'

'What,' asked Onkel Frank irritably, 'is the proposition?'

'The Pitch will cost a hundred pounds for the rest of the Season. I'm offered a quarter-share in profits if I put up twenty-five pounds.'

'Twenty-five pounds?' Onkel Frank sounded scandalised,

as well he might. It was about five hundred pounds in today's money. He lit another Player's. 'Plus I don't suppose you have it, so are we talking academically here?'

'Not entirely,' said the Old Man. 'I have fifteen. I need ten more.'

There was, as they used to say, a pregnant pause.

'You are thinking I might come in with a tenner?'

'I had that in mind, yes. You'd get your share. I reckon my profit on twenty-five quid will be considerable.'

There was another pregnant pause.

'I would not invest in such a hare-brained scheme,' said Onkel Frank. 'Not even with Bad Money.'

'Then,' said the Old Man, 'there is no more to be said.'

'A final thought,' said Onkel Frank. 'Who will own the Rat at the end of the Season? You?'

'Certainly not,' said the Old Man. 'What would I want with a Rat?'

But there was a longing in his voice. He would have loved to own the Rat. Don't ask me why. He just would.

The day the Rat went on show I took my friend Jack to see it. He was taken aback by the garish display cards above the entrance, which read simply, RONNY – THE BIGGEST RAT IN THE WORLD. We did not need to pay to get into the space (a sort of tent) where the Rat was displayed, since the Animal Man was there, clad unexpectedly in a white overall (but still needing a shave), and he grudgingly made room for us. Only six or eight punters could see the Rat at any one time. The admission fee was sixpence, which disappeared into a wooden box presided over by the Animal Man. The smell in the place was that of a strong disinfectant, which was anyway something to be grateful for.

'Nay, bloody hell,' said Jack. 'It's a helluva big Rat, is this.'

The Rat certainly looked bigger than it had in the cage in the hut. I said as much to the Animal Man.

'I've washed its fur in soft soap,' he confided, with a tobacco and beer breath. 'It looks bigger than it is.' His voice held the tones of pride and ownership.

'It looks fine,' I said.

The punters inside giggled and laughed and one of them, a young girl, pushed a piece of chocolate through the wire-netting. The Rat ate it in a flash of huge yellow teeth.

'Nay,' cried the Animal Man, 'can'st not read!' He pointed to a card written in the Old Man's hand. It bore the legend: PLEASE DO NOT FEED OR OTHERWISE MOLEST THIS RAT.

The trippers shrieked with laughter and barged out of the tent. Jack and I followed them. Said Jack as we stood amongst the evening crowds, the wind whipping cool off the sea, 'I've never seen owt like it, have you?'

'No,' I said. I hadn't.

'Do you think they're all right,' he asked, 'keeping an animal in conditions like that? It can't move much.'

'It goes home to the farm every night,' I said. It was something that hadn't occurred to me and I was a bit ashamed of that.

'I mean, there's laws and all sorts about animals,' said Jack. 'How they're kept and all that. I know there is with farm animals. There's heaps of regulations.'

I stared out to sea. The lights on the Central Pier glittered on the water. The trippers in the Song Booths were still singing.

> 'Red Sails in the Sunset,
> Way out on the Sea,

Oh carry my Loved one
Home safely to me . . .'

'I don't suppose it applies to wild animals,' I said. 'Besides, rats are vermin, aren't they?'

As I said the word, I realised that I too was falling under the spell of the Rat. It was in the family. We had money invested in it, or rather the Old Man had.

'Has Percy any money in the Rat?' Jack asked.

'I don't think so,' I said. 'I'm not sure.'

We started to walk home. It was only two-thri miles, as Jack said.

Onkel Frank went to see the Rat. He gazed at it doubtfully and then delivered his opinion. 'That is no rat. I don't know what it is but it's like no rat I've ever seen.'

The Animal Man took exception to these words. 'Don't say that again, Frank. I have money in this and so does Percy.'

'More fool him,' replied Onkel Frank, and with a last long stare at the Rat, repaired to a nearby public house for sustenance. It was almost closing-time and the crowds were standing ten-deep outside the pub. He got himself a whisky and a ginger beer for me, and lit a Player's, moodily.

'The man is some kind of impostor.'

'Who?'

'The Animal Man.'

'In what way?'

'I don't know. What I do know is that he's put an odd fast Dog in, posing as another slow Dog, in his time.'

'How do you know that?'

'Because I'm a handicapper and I know when somebody's Put One In, even if I can't do anything about it.'

'Put a Dog in pretending to be Another Dog?'

'Haven't I just said so?'

That was one question solved: how the Old Man knew Alf. Through the Dog-track. All – or anyway something – was revealed.

'Does Alf own a lot of greyhounds, then?'

'Some. Some he doesn't own. Or pretends he doesn't.'

'Does he make money doing that?'

Onkel Frank looked at me irritably. 'Would he be doing it if he wasn't?'

'He doesn't look rich. He looks poor.'

'Don't go by appearances. Not in this case.'

'It's all I have to go on.'

'Not now. Haven't I just told you he's hot?'

I knew better than to argue with Onkel Frank when he was aggrieved. Which, come to think of it, was most of the time. I offered to buy him another mollifying whisky but the barman inside the pub had shouted time.

'Not worth it. The trippers will drink anything this time of night. The beer's half slops and the whisky's probably watered.'

I remembered the Old Man's warning: never buy beer late on a Saturday night. The best time, if you must drink beer, is on Sunday lunchtime. No landlord dares sell anything but the best stuff then. Everybody is sober, with tongues sharpened by Saturday-night's excesses. Behind us the excess could be heard, in a chorus of *Nellie Dean*, in those days the Chucker Out's Anthem.

> *'By the Old Mill by the Stream*
> *Nellie Dean!*
> *Where we used to sit and dream*

Nellie Dean!
And the Waters as they flow
Seem to murmur soft and low
You're my Heart's Desire,
I love you
Nellie Dean!'

The voices of the long-aproned barmen chanted their final plea: 'D'yer mind, please, ladies and gents, let's be 'aving yer. D'yer mind, *please!*'

Onkel Frank swallowed his whisky. 'This place is a Gold Mine, like everywhere else on the Mile. What I do not understand is why Percy is involved in it. He knows nothing about the fairground business and no matter what happens he'll lose his shirt.'

'I don't think it's the money,' I said.

'What else can it be?'

'I think it's because the Rat is an animal. He's interested in anything to do with animals.'

Onkel Frank considered and rejected this thought.

'Bullshit. He's hoping to make money out of it. I'd be interested to know how much he's actually put in. Do you know?'

I did, but all I said was, 'The Animal Man was asking for twenty-five pounds.'

Onkel Frank digested this. 'Did he get it?'

'As far as I know, yes.'

Onkel Frank was always suspicious of any enterprise with the Old Man in it. Despite his vast intelligence (or perhaps because of it) he was often unable to follow the Old Man's intricate moves, which were based on necessity, not logic.

Earlier that summer the Old Man, temporarily flush from

a large win at the Dogs, had asked Onkel Frank to drop in two weeks' rent at the Landlord's office. What he did not tell Onkel Frank was that he owed ten weeks' rent. The Landlord had (to the Old Man's delight) taken him for the Old Man and delivered a stern lecture about the arrears. Onkel Frank had, in reply, rousted the Landlord with a robust broadside and left the Landlord a puzzled and perplexed man. 'I thought you were him,' he apologised.

'Well, I'm not,' said Onkel Frank. 'So bugger off!'

And left the office.

'I could have sworn,' said the Landlord, who had seen the Old Man only once, when he had paid his original month's rent. The Old Man did not believe in becoming too well-known to possible creditors, occasioning Onkel Frank's summation: 'How that man has escaped a stretch I will never know.'

The Old Man often sailed near the wind, as they used to say, but he never did anything illegal. He often owed money to people but usually to those who, in some way, didn't care enough to pursue him through the Courts. In the Thirties all a landlord could do was evict you and then, as the Old Man said, he was looking at an empty house he couldn't let.

There was an insane logic in all this.

It was nothing either Onkel Frank or I could understand.

Onkel Frank said, in parting, 'One final word. Whatever that animal is, it is no rat!'

And he disappeared into the crowd along the Mile and was lost to sight. I went back into the tent and had a last look at the Rat. There was a queue for it but again I got in free. I remarked on the good business the Rat was doing.

The Animal Man said, 'It's the first time we've been full all day.'

Somehow, I knew he was lying.

But I said nothing. What could I say?

Instead, I peered at the Rat. 'I think he's got fatter.'

'It's the punters. They're always feeding him stuff. Fish and chips, rock, treacle toffee.' As he spoke, a Fat Woman in a paper hat gave the Rat a half-eaten sausage roll. It disappeared in a snap of the Rat's jaws. The Fat Woman started back in alarm.

'Nay, bloody hell, it nearly had me finger off!'

The Animal Man pointed at his sign. 'We tek no responsibility,' he said. 'No responsibility at all.'

'I'd bloody drown it, I would,' said the Fat Woman, who was drunk. 'I'd do away wi' it!'

'Gerroff,' said the Animal Man. 'There's people waiting to see this animal.'

At this the Old Man appeared, as usual unannounced. He said, 'Give the lady her money back, Alf. We don't want dissatisfied customers, do we?'

'Will I buggery,' said the Animal Man.

The Old Man gave the Fat Woman a sixpenny piece, which she took with a gummy smile. 'It's nice to see there's a gentleman left in this world.'

The Old Man raised his hat to her as she left the tent.

'Percy,' said the Animal Man, 'you're One on Your Own!'

'How's business?' asked the Old Man.

'Only very fair,' said the Animal Man.

'Seems pretty busy?'

'First time all day. We're gerrin them as has been chucked out o't pubs now.'

The Old Man peered rather anxiously at the Rat as the punters trooped through behind him.

'Is he all right? He doesn't seem to be moving about much.'

'He's tired,' said the Animal Man. 'It's past his bedtime.'

The Old Man ignored that. He dropped his voice. 'We must be a good few quid in front by now? There must be something to come?'

The Animal Man stared at him. 'Nowt due to you yet, Percy.'

The Old Man looked blank. 'No?'

'Cash in that box, it's what we've taken all day.'

The Old Man didn't look in the box. It contained, perhaps, five pounds.

'I would have thought there was something to come, Alf.'

'Then you'd be wrong.'

'I would have thought, say, a tenner?'

'A tenner? Don't be so bloody daft. A tenner? D'yer know how much my expenses are for this stall?'

'Yes, I do,' said the Old Man. 'You've told me often enough.'

'I'd let thee look at the books,' said the Animal Man with heavy sarcasm, 'only I don't keep any books.'

Said the Old Man, seemingly taking no offence, 'Well, if you say there's nothing to come, there's nothing to come, is there?'

'Thart reet in that, any road.'

There was no mistaking the dismissal in the Animal Man's voice. He looked at the fading trickle of punters and suddenly shouted, 'Hurry it up, will yer? I'm closing up for the neet soon!' He looked at the Old Man. 'Move out the way, Percy.'

The Old Man was looking at the Rat again. He was stooping very low to get a good view of it. The Rat seemed to be breathing very heavily.

'Are you sure this animal is all right?' he asked the Animal Man.

'No, I'm not, and I don't care if it's aw reet or not, so long as it's here to show to these mugs tomorrow neet!'

The Old Man ignored that.

'What food are you giving it?'

'What I give my dogs.' The Animal Man took a stick and poked the Rat in the ribs. It moved slowly but made no noise. 'Any more questions?'

The Old Man straightened up with a sigh. 'No. I'll bid you goodnight, Alf.'

'Aye. An' Good Neet ta Thee, an' all.'

As we left we could hear him shouting, 'One last chance, Folks! See the Biggest Rat in the World!'

We stood on the Prom, thick with drunken men and women, roaring and shrieking and singing their way home to the boarding-houses behind the Central Station. In this maelstrom, the Old Man was a calm centre, as he stood, puffing on his Churchman's, his hat at a rakish angle, his Fusiliers' tie bright against his white collar.

'He was very rude,' I said. 'Is he drunk?'

'Yes, I would say so. I'd say he's been drunk all day. He has nothing to do, you see, but take the money. No chance to spend it.'

'Drunk in charge of a Rat?' I said.

'Exactly,' said the Old Man. But he wasn't smiling.

Before we got on the tram to go home, he made a tuppenny telephone call from the public box near the Pier. I don't know who he spoke to but the local Sanitation Officer raided the Stall the next evening and impounded the Rat. The Animal Man was fined Fifty Pounds – a fortune then – at the local Magistrate's Court, the following day, for Keeping an Animal in Cruel and Insanitary Conditions.

'Why did you do it?' I asked the Old Man.

'Had to. He wasn't going to pay me what I was due. He's a villain.'

'Will he know you made that call?'

'He might guess.'

'What will happen to the Rat?'

The Old Man suddenly looked very agitated. He got to his feet and left the house in a hurry. When he got back he treated himself to a large whisky and water. I had not seen him so upset for a long time, not since he had lost a lot of money he didn't have at Towcester the previous year.

'What happened?'

'They've put the Rat down.'

I said, 'Well, it was only a rat, wasn't it? Only vermin?'

'It wasn't a rat according to the Sanitation people, it was a Coypu. That's an American animal, very like a rat but a lot bigger. God knows how the Animal Man got it!'

'Well, in that case, perhaps it's for the best all round,' I said. 'If it was a native American animal it probably couldn't survive in this country.'

'Who knows?' The Old Man blinked rapidly. 'I would personally have let it loose on the Moss, to take its chances. That would have been fair to everybody, especially the animal, don't you agree?'

'Yes,' I said.

'I Wish I Was, Mister Withers'

Ted got himself a Motor-bike.

It was a Norton and it stood in the scullery, on newspapers spread on the floor, and we all stood and admired it. The bike was something to admire. It was all chrome and black paint and it could go sixty miles an hour.

We all had a go on the pillion.

I learned to swerve into the swing of it. The Old Man got off hastily, pointing out a dog walking leisurely across the road half a mile in front. He walked home.

Ted, in his leather coat and flying brilliantined hair, was my idol, as all Big Brothers should be. I was delighted he had the bike. He'd always wanted one.

The Old Man was delighted, too. But mostly he was puzzled. For that Bike cost Sixty Pounds, new. Where had Ted got it?

Ted had no regular job now, since the Books on Wheels had packed up. He picked up the odd job at the Dogs and he'd been down as far South as Romford and as far West as Belfast on sales-jobs that were, in the end, farces, as so many young men's jobs were in the late Thirties. He was bright, good-looking, and qualified to do a job nobody wanted him to do.

I suppose in a way he was waiting for the War. We all were. Hitler was on the march.

Onkel Frank kept us up to date with his progress.

Without doubt, he knew more about Adolf Hitler than British Intelligence. Which wasn't saying much. They seemed to think 'He' was no danger. Onkel Frank applied the morals of the Race-track to the Warlord. 'Have you seen what He's done *now*?' It was always He with a capital H.

Unlike most people, Onkel Frank, who had read everything, had read what Hitler had read. Nietzsche and Schopenhauer and all the rest. He was familiar with Hitler's views on Euthanasia and the Perfect Race because lots of intellectuals of the time, like Shaw, more or less believed them, too. Shaw's Superman is Hitler's Superman, but Shaw only used actors and Hitler used people, said Onkel Frank.

'The Man means business,' he never tired of admonishing us, as if we could do anything about it. The Rhineland, Austria, Czechoslovakia, Munich, none of us believed there was a way out of War. Fourteen to forty, we knew we would be in it.

My employer, Leonard, didn't see why we should.

'All nations are different,' said Leonard, standing with his back to the gas-fire, smoking his cigarette. 'The Chinaman can live on a bowl of rice a day. The Germans and ourselves are different and need a little more.'

'Hitler will attack us,' I said. 'It's just a matter of when.'

Said Leonard, and he spoke for most people in Blackpool of the employing-class, 'He just wants the best for Germany. I've been there and, believe me, he's changed the look of the place. No unemployed on street corners. A job and a full dinner-pail.'

I couldn't say anything to that. I hadn't seen what he had. I had only Onkel Frank's diatribes to go on. That, and what had been happening in Spain and Austria and Czechoslovakia. But I was only sixteen, so what did I know? What could I know?

Nobody wanted War. They pushed it out of their minds.

In that Summer of 1939 they started going to the Dogs again and betting money in larger sums than for years.

'The Rush of the Gadarene Swine,' said Onkel Frank.

'How so?' I asked.

'Subconsciously, they know War is coming. It has to, after Munich. So they're out for a good time before it comes.' He paused. 'It'll be poison gas, of course. The first day.'

He was wrong about that. Churchill was ready to use poison gas after Dunkirk. Hitler never was, even on the Russian Front. Even when his generals promoted the idea. But then, he had been gassed in the First World War. Also, he wasn't as desperate as Churchill in 1940.

None of us knew any of that, then. We expected Armageddon. Simple as that.

Meantime, Ted has this new motor-bike and, as the Old Man mused, 'Where has he got the money from?'

Nobody knew. Except that it had to be from the Dogs. But how?

This puzzled the Old Man so much that he forgot to feed the animals in the yard and had to hurriedly do it before going up to the Evening-meeting himself. Although the four rabbits, the six mice and the pigeon were supposed to be mine, the Old Man owned them, really. He had experienced an Edwardian childhood, most of the time in the country, where he had worn long knickerbockers and ice-skated with wooden skates and kept linnets and pigeons and dogs and bird-egged and did everything that a middle-class boy did then.

The rabbits and the mice and the rest were there to keep him in touch with a Golden Time, before Wars and Money and Women had complicated his life. It did seem as if it was a good time to be a boy in, far better than mine. He cleaned and fed the animals and released the pigeon daily from the makeshift loft in the scrap of back garden. 'It's lost its homing instinct,' he said, cupping it in his hand. 'It'll stay here until it dies or a cat gets it.'

'Smout?' I enquired.

'Certainly not Smout,' he said, testily for once.

Smout (Auld Scots for Small Fry) had been so named by my Uncle the Scotch Comic years before. Smout had only half a tail, having got it trapped in our neighbour Mrs Kirkham's rat-trap.

'That bloody woman,' said the Old Man between gritted teeth when he saw her in the street. But he always raised his hat.

He fed Smout on Butcher's 'lights' chopped up into squares about the size of Oxo cubes. He boiled these cubes in an old pan. The smell of the food drove the cat wild. For the very good reason that he had probably forgotten to feed it for a couple of days.

Finally, he would call, 'That's enough, Cat!' and pour the meat cubes into a colander to drain off the horrid-smelling juice, then on to a plate. But the cat was by now clawing, demented, at him, so he would scatter the cubes along the floor of the scullery. They bounced, having the consistency of rubber, and the cat jumped and clawed at them, attempting to swallow them whole, no matter how hot they were.

'Bloody cat can't wait,' he said.

The cat followed him everywhere, like a dog. Now, it stood, bemused, as the Old Man boiled its latest feed. It could not very well run after the cubes now, because Ted's Bike stood in the kitchen again, after its trial run.

'Where *did* he get it?' The Old Man mused, again.

'At the motor-dealer's,' I said.

'I am speaking of the money to buy it.' The Old Man had a thoughtful look on his face. He plainly thought Ted had backed a huge winner and said nothing.

The truth about the Bike was something different. And it did not emerge until it was all over.

Ted was like the Brothers. He was no fool and he had an eye on the main chance, as they used to say. Unlike me, he didn't find the gambling and its consequences amusing and yet to be kept at a distance. He joined in, but very quietly and without flamboyance. In that, he was unlike his Brother-in-law and golfing companion, Matt, who usually bought so many Tote tickets at the Dogs (using some system or other) that, in the words of Onkel Frank, 'He doesn't know himself which animal he wants to win.'

Endearing, but no way for a Serious Person to behave, was what Onkel Frank was saying.

Ted was a Serious Person.

He had taken in, during his time in Edwards' office, all that he could learn about prices and odds and the thousand things you have to know if you are ever going to make money racing. Because Out There on the Race-tracks are thousands of the smartest people in the country, and they lose money at it.

Ted had one thing over them. He wasn't a mad gambler, like Matt or the Old Man. He was a Thinker and a Watcher. Sometimes if you are a Thinker and a Watcher on a Race-track, you see something.

Ted saw something.

He saw a small team of men, not local, Londoners as far as he could tell from their voices, making large bets up and down the line of Bookies, just before the Off. He did nothing until he had seen them with money a good number of times. They never backed more than two dogs at any meeting and they did it, as the phrase had it, in their stocking-feet. That is to say, quietly and without fuss.

Ted thought about that. Then he proposed, innocently, that he and I go up to Newcastle to see Marthaann one weekend. I would go with him anywhere, so I agreed. We went up on the train on a Saturday and came back late on the Sunday.

The Old Man wondered what it was all about, but didn't object. After all, we hadn't seen Marthaann for the best part of a year, so it wasn't out of the way.

Marthaann never came to Blackpool any more. She had given up on anybody wanting anything to do with the Shell-fish Shops. Ted didn't want them, nor did Peggy, who was anyway married and away in Manchester now. But the topic was sure to be raised by Marthaann, and it was, as soon as we got there and had finished a splendid lunch of beef and Yorkshire pudding with tinned peaches and cream to follow.

Marthaann lived well. The new house was a semi-detached in Walkerville, one of the new suburbs of the city, small by the standards of Isaac's old Victorian house, where we'd all lived before we went to Blackpool on a holiday that had now lasted six years.

'Strathclair' was named for her Henderson brothers and sisters, who lived in a place of that name in Manitoba. She was the only one of them left in England. Even her Mother had gone. She must have been lonely but she wouldn't have admitted to anything like that. She had filled the house with leather suites and fitted carpets and good crockery and feather quilts and the best sensible money could buy.

It was, she said, Our Home. It was always there if we wanted it. Of course it came at a price. Even I knew that.

The Shops.

'Even in these terrible times, I'm doing well,' Marthaann said, filling our teacups with more strong tea as we sat, sated, before a splendid coal-fire. 'Those Shops have been a Godsend. If only I knew somebody was prepared to take them on when I go, I'd sleep better in my bed of a night.'

Ted said, 'You look very well, just the same, Mother.'

Marthaann glowed, then frowned. Ted had been the apple of her eye, as the Book says, and even he had joined the Enemy, represented by the Old Man.

'Nobody cares whether I'm well or ill, young fellow.'

'They do, Mother,' Ted protested. He actually felt a lot of affection for her. He'd known her as a young wife, suffering from the Old Man's spendthrift ways and neglect. I hadn't. She'd always had the Shops and was busy as a bee, as I remembered her. Like all working mothers, she had lost out with me to what nowadays they call The Carer. That is to say, Jane. It wasn't her fault but it was a fact.

Ted was trying to explain what he was there for, but it wasn't easy, whatever it was. I was pretty sure there was some design behind his visit. Ted did few things by chance. He had been taught, much more than I had, by Onkel Frank and the Old Man. He was ten years older than me and much more influenced by them. 'We came up to see you, just to see how you're getting along.'

Marthaann said, 'Are you in a job?'

'Not really,' said Ted. 'Not at the moment, no.'

'Not hanging around that Dog-track with your Father?'

'Not really, no.' He never missed a meeting.

'How people can work at such a place I don't know.'

'No, Mother.'

Ted picked up jobs Clerking or Running About (advising Bookies on Prices along the line): anything he could. He was serving a thorough apprenticeship, the only one open to him, with always the promise – slim but there – of Big Money, if he got lucky.

Marthaann poured more tea and pressed Cadbury's Milk Tray on us. Ted refused and smoked his Player's but I ate my way steadily through the box. I was at the age when I was always hungry. I was tall for my age and doing a job and playing a lot of cricket and football and studying in my spare time as well. Sleep came last. I dozed off in front of the fire.

I wakened to hear Marthaann saying, 'I'm sure that boy doesn't get enough to eat. His Father never sat down to a proper meal all the time I lived with him. Always in a hurry.'

Ted said, 'He's all right. He's the youngest player in the Under-Twenty-Ones' Football League.'

I was. I got tonked about enough to prove it.

Some of the Under-Twenty-Ones of the Sunday School League were over twenty-one by a distance. Some were the fathers of families. When they tackled you, you knew about it. The boys in my team had humble jobs. Sugar Boilers. Labourers. French-polishers. The left-winger was the Curate,

Mr Slater, bald at thirty, dirty player, reprimanded twice by referees for Bad Language and very popular in consequence.

Ted didn't tell Marthaann that I usually came off the pitch black and blue, a testimony to the remark made by our Trainer that I'd get more medals on my legs than I would on my watch-chain. That was because I was a cleverish player and sometimes held on to the ball to show how clever I was. The Sunday School League had a short way with players like that.

Ted played Golf and naturally Snooker, and that was it.

Like Marthaann's relatives, the Hendersons, who represented Canada at one time or another in just about everything (Marthaann's cousin ran in Hitler's Berlin Games of 1936), I had a sporting gene. But nobody knew about genes then.

The Old Man had never played any competitive sport apart from hockey when he was an Officer Cadet at Oxford. He scored three goals for the Cadets against an England Eleven. The Captain of the England Eleven asked the Old Man if he was a Colonial, since he'd never come across him playing in England. The Old Man said, 'I've only been playing this Season.' The Captain was astonished and gave him his card. 'Come and see me after the War, if we both get through it. You're a bloody marvel.'

'Why didn't you bother?' I asked the Old Man.

'No point, much. Besides, the feet went wrong on me.'

'But why were you so good at hockey?'

'I was fit and fast and I shot for goal every time. That was about it.'

'Didn't you want to do any more of it?'

'No. Why should I?'

Obviously, apart from that errant episode, I had the Henderson genes in all sorts of ways. Since most of the Hendersons turned out to be rich as well as sporty, that, said Marthaann, was no bad thing.

'They've done well in Canada,' she said. 'I should have gone with them. There's nothing here for me.'

'You've got the Shops,' said Ted. It was his first false move. Marthaann went for the kill. 'Would you think again about coming into them? I'd make you a partner.'

'Mother, I'd be useless,' said Ted, smiling his charming smile. 'It simply isn't Me.'

'The same attitude as your father,' said Marthaann. 'It's beneath you to get your hands dirty at anything.'

'It isn't that,' said Ted. It was.

But who *could* want it? As Peggy said, you could smell the fish on yourself, no matter how much you washed, no matter how much scent you used. It got in your hair and under your nails.

Marthaann gave up for the moment. She would return to the attack. We knew that.

We slept in downy covers and wakened to the scent of bacon and eggs. We ate heartily and then admired the garden and the road – 'A respectable district,' said Marthaann. 'Very exclusive' – and made all the right noises, and still Ted had not shown his hand, whatever it was.

And we had to catch the two o'clock train from Newcastle Central Station. It would get us back in Blackpool, via Carlisle, at ten o'clock that night.

By midday Marthaann had made us packets of sandwiches and pressed a thermos of tea on us and we were ready to go. We would catch a bus at the top of the road. Marthaann didn't like goodbyes at Railway Stations. They reminded her of the Old Man and the War.

Ted made his pitch then, asking me, in a low voice, to

have a look at the garden. I left the kitchen door open but I couldn't hear much. Ted was talking and he seemed (as far as I could make out) to be saying he'd consider going into the Shops, but not yet, he had a business prospect in view and that was something he wanted to talk to her about.

The door suddenly closed and I heard no more.

Marthaann saw us off at the bus with a wave and a tear in her eye. Ted seemed affected, too.

I said, 'We're cutting it fine.'

We caught the train all right. Ted said little the whole journey. He slept a bit and read a Sunday paper, the *News of the World*. I found it interesting, but beyond my understanding. The people in it all seemed mad.

Then I too fell asleep.

Ted went to the Dogs with the twenty pounds he had borrowed from Marthaann. He followed the Team of men laying money on selected dogs at the Death, that is, just before the Off. Not getting too close to them, just close enough to see what they were backing and then backing it himself. He did this successfully, he told me, after I asked him what had happened to the money Marthaann had given him.

He swore me to secrecy.

Naturally I swore to it. He was my Big Brother.

All went well, Ted told, until one day, having a cup of tea in the Stadium tea-room, one of the men suddenly appeared in front of him. This man was as broad as he was long and he had a broken nose and broken teeth. He spoke, as convicts do, out of the corner of his mouth. His tone was easy, conversational.

'Know what we're doing, don'tcher?'

156

Ted thought for a moment. 'Yes, I think I do.'

'You talked about this to anybody?'

'No.'

'Not to your Uncles? Not to . . . Percy?'

'Last one I'd talk to.'

'You do realise we could take steps?'

'I know you could.'

The man was quiet for a long time, just looking at Ted. Then he said, 'We've made enquiries about you and you come well-recommended. What we do is this. You meet me here, every meeting, same time, quarter of an hour before racing, and I give you the name of a Dog. You have, top, a tenner on it, and you spread that tenner about, not all to the same Bookie. All right?'

Ted could not reply. He just nodded and swallowed.

For a whole Season he backed a winner nearly every Meeting. He didn't know where the information was coming from and he didn't ask.

One day the Man said, 'It's all over now, Son. Be lucky.'

Again, Ted just nodded.

I said, 'Weren't you scared? All the time?'

'I thought I'd die.'

I said, 'It was brave.' It was.

Ted said, 'Anyway, I got the Bike out of it.'

The Old Man could never understand that Bike. Nobody ever told him. I certainly didn't.

Ted lived on the remainder of the money for a long time. He gambled judiciously, following Frank's tips, and showed a small profit. He roared around on the Motor-bike, from the Lake District to the Peaks to the Yorkshire Dales, with his girl-friend, Gladys, a pretty brunette (as they said then), on the pillion. They ate at farmhouses and had a good time, exploring the hills and dales. Then, suddenly, Ted got rid of the oil-stained leather coat and sold the motor-bike. The girl had a well-to-do father, and riding about on Nortons and living on your wits at Dog-tracks was, as they say now, unacceptable.

Events moved quickly after that. Somehow Ted got a job, a real job, with a small car attached to it, selling furniture for a large chainstore, a good job. He got married. He and his young wife lived in a small flat. He didn't go to the Dogs any more. I wondered why he would go into the furniture business to please his wife when he wouldn't go into the Prawn Shops to please his mother.

I never knew the answer to that, except that furniture doesn't smell and wives are more winning than mothers.

In the September of 1939, Ted became a father and we came back from the church where the little girl had been baptised Beatrice to hear Mr Chamberlain tell us that we were at War with Germany.

We listened to that in silence. We looked at each other and at the Baby. Ted and Gladys, Peg and Matt, the Old Man and me. Nobody knew what to say.

I thought of screaming bombs, poison gas, the Trenches. Still nobody spoke.

Mr Withers, Ted's father-in-law, a large, normally morose man, who could neither read nor write but, as the Old Man said, certainly knew how many beans made five, plainly felt something was called for, a comment, something.

He said to the Old Man, whom he had met only once before, at the wedding . . . 'Well, I'm Made Up, Mr Prior.' By this, he meant he never had to think about money again.

The Old Man considered this statement, then said courteously, 'I wish I was, Mr Withers.'

'I'm glad young Ted got rid of that Motor-bike,' said Mr Withers.

'I never knew why he ever got it,' said the Old Man absently. 'Or how.'

And that is how we all went to War.

'They Throw It At You'

Harry Norris ran a small carpet shop on Highfield Road. He sold a few carpets but subsisted mainly on repairs to those frayed and dusty axminsters already laid down in people's front rooms. He sold a few rolls of cheap lino a week to landladies whose husbands would lay it themselves, and that was about it.

The Old Man reported that Harry had married a woman with more money than he had, which was not necessarily very much. Enough, however, for her family to complain of Harry's lack of commercial enterprise. 'He must,' the Old man reflected, 'be the poorest Jew in Blackpool.'

In those days the Synagogue would have been hard pressed to field a hundred people, but they all knew one another, which meant they all knew Harry and they all knew he was a failure.

Which was why Harry sought out the Old Man's company. That, and the fact that Harry liked a bet.

He rarely missed a meeting at the Dogs, closing down his business early every Wednesday and Saturday to make sure he was at St Anne's Road for the First Race.

His immediate task was to obtain from Onkel Frank his

selection of Winners and Losers for the meeting. Harry knew nothing of the intricacies of gambling and was strictly a mug punter. He had, however, the respect of his race for learning.

'You model yourself on your Uncle Frank,' he advised me. 'He has Brains, all those sums he does.'

'He doesn't seem to get very rich on it, Mr Norris.'

'Young man, you sound like my wife.'

Harry, like all gamblers, pretended he won money racing.

'Frank's in the Ministry of Whatsit, isn't he?' said Harry. 'What a waste!'

One of the minor disasters of the War, now on for a long 'Phoney' winter, was the fact that it had put Onkel Frank at a desk at the Ministry of Pensions. Hundreds of clerks were housed in a large, deserted hotel on Blackpool's North Shore. I had made the mistake of asking Onkel Frank what the people (many of them lower-grade clerks who had lived in London inner-suburbs all their lives and hated Breezy Blackpool) were like.

'Not one in a hundred has had an original thought in his life! Does that answer your question?'

It didn't, but it told me Onkel Frank didn't care for the Civil Service. Well, he wouldn't. He had worked all his life where speed and accuracy and imagination and daring were the qualities most in demand. Civil Servants of the lower grades do not possess these qualities. To him, their careful, pettifogging procedures were a mark of stupidity. The truth was and is that Civil Servants, however lowly, aren't allowed to make mistakes because they speak for the Government. So they do everything twice and many do it slowly, and some play even safer and never do it at all.

Onkel Frank found this intolerable.

However, there was a ray of light. The Principal Officer

of the Ministry discovered that Onkel Frank was a Racing Handicapper. He himself was a tireless and luckless gambler. But he could not get through a day without a bet. If he did not have a bet, the Principal Officer's day was a desert.

Onkel Frank found him two horses or two dogs a day, to back.

The Principal Officer was a happier man and a richer one. Or anyway, not a poorer one.

Anybody who followed Onkel Frank's tips was likely to make money, or anyway not lose much. Onkel Frank took good care of that, calculating long into the blacked-out nights, with Florrie gone to bed, and a whisky bottle at his elbow, if he could afford it, strong black tea if he couldn't, the Race Cards and Form Books piled in front of him, the foolscap blackening with his calculations.

In the end, the Principal Officer arranged for Onkel Frank to have a small office of his own, where he could perform this task in working hours. What else he did, if anything, he never said. So much for his contribution to the War Effort. 'About the same as in the First War,' said the Old Man. 'Hardly recordable on any known scale.'

Harry Norris was not 'directed' into office or factory, being over fifty years of age, and somehow, at any rate in that first winter of the War, when nothing seemed to change except for food-rationing and the Black Out, he seemed untouched by it all. His shop had a couple of second-hand carpets for sale in the window, and a few pathetic rolls of lino stood propped against the wall inside. When I went into the shop, Harry always seemed to be perusing the Racing Page. The only racing going on was in the Irish Republic, and of course at the Dogs, which were on only twice a week. I would deliver my message (usually an envelope containing Onkel

Frank's tips) and was often rewarded with a cup of lemon tea and a piece of walnut cake. Harry explained that the lemon in the tea was ersatz. Nobody had seen a lemon for months. I drank it out of politeness.

Harry had advice for me. 'Keep away from the Women.' He lowered his voice and whispered, 'Don't get into the marriage business too soon. It's murder.'

I was of an age when the idea of marriage, or anyway the idea of a woman all to oneself, seemed a highly desirable condition, but I did not say so.

'It's a mug's game,' said Harry, champing on the walnut cake, which tasted odd because of the combination of War-time flour, ersatz lemon and no walnuts. 'I left it as long as I could, I can tell you.'

I knew Harry had two small children and to me he seemed very old indeed. Obviously he had left it very late. I did not think somehow that I could leave it as long as he had. Anyway, I hoped not.

'If you go into a marriage without a decent business behind you, or some real money, the woman's dowry becomes too important, you see?'

I didn't, but I nodded.

When Older People talked to me, I knew it wasn't expected that I should say anything. I was supposed to be flattered if they talked to me at all. Harry said, 'I tell you, young man, get yourself very well established in business first. Then you don't need to kowtow to anybody, especially your wife's relatives.'

At this point his wife came into the shop.

She seemed a pleasant-enough woman, and was enquiring if more tea was required. When Harry said it wasn't, she smiled at me and went back into the kitchen.

Harry said, 'The relatives think you're a sponger, they think you married the woman for the dowry. They let you know what they think about you without saying a word.'

I nodded sympathetically. I hadn't the foggiest idea what Harry was talking about, but I supposed that his friendship with the Old Man in some way compensated for the lack of it in his wife's family.

For a friendship it certainly was.

Harry would present himself at the house, consulting his pocket-watch, admonishing the Old Man for his lateness, every time the Old Man played a Money Match at Snooker. He would carry the Old Man's cue, and busily pay the tram-fares and take control of the whole of the evening's business: the state of the cloth on the match-table, the lighting from the central shade on to the table, the elbow-room for cueing; all of this was noticed and reported on to the Old Man who, as usual, was not listening to anybody he didn't have to listen to, but nodding politely now and again, wondering whether he should back himself to win and how much for.

That was always the rub.

The Old Man was an excellent prospect at Snooker's lower levels, the Pub Handicap Leagues. He had a profound knowledge of the game, particularly of the table's angles (having learned Billiards first, something players nowadays never do), and nerves of steel in a crisis. Or, put another way, he didn't really care whether he won or lost, so more often than not he won. Even when he should have lost.

This cavalier attitude to serious business often upset his opponents. They had always been 'cased' by Harry, who would sometimes journey alone to a faraway snooker game in St Anne's or Lytham, to get a look at the Old Man's next opponent. To the Old Man he would report, 'This fellow is a potter, Percy, you have to leave him nothing, absolutely nothing, Percy, or he'll shop it, as sure as I'm sitting here!'

The Old Man sighed. He had been out-potting potters all his life.

'Well, we'll see, Harry,' he would reply.

'We haven't got to see, Percy,' Harry would admonish him. 'We have to leave the man nothing. Absolutely nothing. Or we'll lose our money.'

When Harry said 'our money', he meant *his* money.

Harry had a belief in the Old Man that touched idolatry, and wagered on him in a gallant and blinkered manner, despite the Old Man's protests.

'I'm no certainty to beat this fellow,' the Old Man would say.

'Lissen Percy, lissen, I'm telling you, this man has no chance against you, none whatever, none at all when you are playing your best game.'

Harry would stare at the Old Man through his glasses (done up on one side with insulation tape), wearing his aged black homburg hat and his old gabardine mac. 'All you have to do, Percy, all I'm asking you to do, is to play a little safety. Not all the time, no, just now and then, so this man doesn't get into his stride. If he gets into his stride, Percy, he can pot a few balls. I saw him last week at the Working Men's Club at St Anne's; beat the best player they have, he's made a lot of big breaks, Percy—'

But the Old Man was suddenly absent, having got up and strolled across to the bar to buy for himself a whisky, and for Harry a small sherry. No man in any bar in Blackpool drank sherry, except Harry Norris. The Old Man bought the sherry and put it wordlessly down on the bar-table. Harry nodded, sipped the sherry with a painful grimace, and laid out the Old Man's chalk on the side of the Billiard-table, and took his cue out of its case. Then he produced a clean pocket-handkerchief for the Old Man to wipe the perspiration from his cue, for the Old Man's hands often sweated when he played, his only sign of any form of stress. In fact the Old Man played almost by rote, hardly ever coming across a shot he hadn't played before. This bored him, and accounted for his occasional, wildly optimistic potting sprees, which reduced Harry to agonies of anxiety.

'Percy, No, No, No . . . !' he would whisper. 'The Green! Go safe off the Green . . . *Percy!*'

But the man had not been born who could tell the Old Man which ball to play. Constitutionally, the Old Man was a risk-taker and Harry was not. So the lost chances plunged Harry into deep despair and he closed up like a clam in a glass of whisky (as the Old Man said), his anguish turning to ecstasy when the Old Man's risky play came off and the Yellow, Green, Brown, Blue, Pink and Black went into the pockets like bullets and – once again – the Old Man had saved a lost cause.

Harry collected his bets money then.

He bought a large whisky for the Old Man, a shandy for me, and nothing for himself, and shook the Old Man's hand, his eyes shining. 'I said to the Boy here, Percy is going to pot this man off the table! I said it to you, didn't I?'

He hadn't, but I nodded.

'I said to the Boy, Percy will win it, even if he needs all the colours! Don't worry about Percy, I said to the Boy, he never lets you down, he's the Man for the Moment!'

'Good Health, Harry,' said the Old Man mildly, sipping his whisky and reaching over to shake his defeated and dazed opponent's hand. 'Good game. You were very unlucky.'

'There's nobody like Percy,' said Harry to me. 'He's One On His Own!'

His eyes shone when he said it.

That was how they were, then, Harry and the Old Man.

The Old Man got an offer of a job. That was something he viewed with concern.

I was in the house when Freddy Douthwaite called. Freddy ran a newsagent's shop in the Winter and had two stalls on the Amusement Park in the Summer, one Outdoors, one Indoors. That way, the trippers played one of your Games, rain or shine. With the shop to see him through the Winter, Freddy Douthwaite had, as he said to the Old Man, by way of opening the conversation, a 'Good Goin' On'.

The Old Man listened, bored, to this. He disliked the North-country way of talking about possessions and money, not because he hadn't much of either, but because he considered it poor manners. He forgave Freddy Douthwaite, his sigh inferred, because he was a decent-enough fellow in his way and had lost a hand in the War.

Freddy's hand was encased in leather, like a small boxing-glove, and indeed Freddy seemed rather like a furious little bantam-weight, with his ferrety red face, his trilby hat nailed to his head and his aggressive, pugnacious manner.

'Nah then, Percy,' he was saying to the Old Man. 'I'm fixed up wi' as much as I can manage, wi' the Darts Inside and the Ride Outside. I can't take any more on and look after it properly, can I?'

'No,' said the Old Man, gazing absently at the clock, which told him Racing had started at Leopardstown. He sighed. 'No, I don't suppose you can.'

'I know of a good thing going,' said Freddy, lowering his

167

voice and ignoring me, as they all did. I was reading some English for my Correspondence Course and thus seemed harmless, far removed from the stern business of making money.

The Old Man brightened at the idea of a Good Thing.

'Where's it running? Leopardstown?'

'No, it is not running at Leopardstown', said Freddy Douthwaite irritably. 'I'm not talking about a horse, Percy.'

'Ah,' said the Old Man, losing interest again.

'What I'm on about,' Freddy Douthwaite's face seemed redder than ever with the exertion of gaining the Old Man's attention. 'What I'm on about is that there's a Game going at the Park. It's a right good 'un, it's the Drop the Man in the Water Game, Percy!'

I looked up from my books. I knew the Stall, or Game as Freddy called it. It consisted of a Stooge sitting on a swing balanced over a large pond of water. Above his head was a Bull's Eye. At Three Balls for a Tanner, the Punters aimed at the Bull's Eye. If they hit it, the Man on the Swing fell into the water, to general hilarity and awful shrieks from the women punters. It didn't happen often, but even so the Man on the Swing was thought to have the worst job on the Park.

He had to be paid extra for it.

But that was all right. The Game took a lot of money.

'Is it?' asked the Old Man mildly. 'Well, I'm damned.'

Freddy Douthwaite's voice dropped until it was almost inaudible. 'It's yours if you want it, Percy!'

The Old Man looked alarmed, as well he might.

Said Freddy Douthwaite, 'What d'you think about that?'

It was not difficult to see what the Old Man thought about it. Not much, was what he thought about it. He lit a Churchman's while he thought not very much about it. He offered one to Freddy Douthwaite.

'Took your breath away did that, eh?' asked Freddy Douthwaite, refusing the Churchman's and lighting a Park Drive. 'I knew it would. I said to myself, it'll tek Percy's breath away when I tell him, it will that.'

'It is a surprise, certainly,' said the Old Man.

'Well, when you said to me things were a bit umpty, I knew you weren't talking about working for me or owt like that.'

'No, not exactly,' said the Old Man.

He had once worked on a Game but so much money had stuck to his fingers that he had only lasted the one day, being paid off without comment at the day's end. What had possessed him to do the job, since he hated all jobs that had set hours, I never knew. The point was, all workers in all Games pocketed a proportion of the money that passed through their hands. The Bosses, like Freddy Douthwaite, knew they were doing it. They knew to a penny how much every Attendant was taking – Freddy Douthwaite's boxing-glove of a hand struck them in the pocket, supposedly accidentally (to ascertain what amount of coinage they had pocketed), so often that one or two had been known to call out, 'Low blow, Freddy!'

At which Freddy Douthwaite would put his furious red face in theirs and shout in his hoarse voice: 'Do I look after you on this job?'

The Attendants would nod, po-faced.

'Do I let you Go for a Drink, two-thri times a night?'

Again, the Attendants would nod.

'Do I pay you the Going Rate?'

Again, the nod.

Freddy Douthwaite would take a deep breath.

'Then Play the Game!' he would shout, hoarsely. 'Play the Bloody Game!'

And the boxing-glove would tap them in the region of their private parts, the coin in their pockets would jingle, and (said the Attendants) Freddy Douthwaite would calculate, to a shilling, what they had stolen in the course of the evening.

The point was, there was an acceptable percentage. The Old Man had wildly overstepped it.

Well, he would.

In point of fact, I'd been glad he'd given up such a menial job. I didn't like my schoolfriends catching sight of him.

Of course, it was a better job than the Man on the Swing, who drank a lot to get over the humiliation of it all. But *he* had the worst job in Blackpool.

'You'll be taking it on then, Freddy?' the Old Man hazarded.

'No. It's just what I'm not doing. Like I say, it's yours if you want it.'

'How can it be?' asked the Old Man. 'There's a waiting list for Games, isn't there?'

There was. Everybody knew that the Games were money in the Bank.

They were also hard work. Nobody knew that better than the Old Man.

He shifted uneasily as Freddy Douthwaite said, in an even lower voice, 'Of course there's a waiting list, there's always a waiting list, but there's a War On now and half the fellas who run Stalls and Games and Rides are in the Army or on Munitions.' Freddy drew on his Park Drive, cupped by long habit in his hand, out of sight of overseers and officers. 'These Games are all rented out, you know that as well as I do. But nobody knows how many punters there'll be this summer, the War being on.'

'Yes,' said the Old Man, seeing a ray of hope. 'Perhaps nobody will come at all?'

Freddy Douthwaite shook his head. 'This isn't a Proper War like you and me was in, Percy. This is what they call a Non Event.'

It was true. The Phoney War was on.

War had been declared in the September. There was a Black Out and shortages of all kinds of food. But there was work, in War Factories opening up all over the place, and a general air of cheerfulness. People were better off and they had an aim in life.

They called it the Phoney War because nobody did much about it except the Air Force and the Navy. The radio played *We're Gonna Hang Out the Washing on the Siegfried Line.*

The Old Man, who had a proper respect for the Germans, said, 'A mite optimistic, I'd say.'

He had been to Manchester for an interview. He was on the Army Officer's Emergency Reserve but, as my Sister Peggy put it, the Reserve would have to be exhausted before they sent for the Old Man.

However, he lived in hope. He had loved the Army, not the killing part but the Order and Comradeship part. The fact was, he was over fifty. He was telling Freddy Douthwaite in an effort to head him off, 'The Army might send for me, y'know, Freddy.'

Freddy Douthwaite shook his head. 'We're a coupla owd crocks, Percy, they won't want the like of us.'

'They might,' said the Old Man.

Freddy Douthwaite shook his head. 'Nivver in this world.'

They smoked in silence a moment, united in their soldiers'

memories. They had both seen a lot of fighting but they did not seem saddened by it.

I thought that very strange at the time, but I don't now.

Freddy Douthwaite said, 'It's going, is the Stall, on a Yearly Rental, Percy.'

'The money would be high?' said the Old Man, hopefully.

'It is,' admitted Freddy Douthwaite.

'What kind of sum are we talking about?' asked the Old Man, who had no intention, I knew, of buying it, no matter the price.

Freddy Douthwaite leaned even closer to the Old Man. 'It's two hundred quid for the Season.'

There was a reverent silence at the mention of such a large sum. Even the Old Man was impressed.

'It's a lot of money,' said the Old Man, his eye straying to the clock on the mantelpiece. Racing had started at Leopardstown.

'You can get it, for that price.' Freddy Douthwaite's voice was now of even higher intensity. 'Your brother would lend it to you?'

The Old Man clutched at this straw. 'No chance there, I'm afraid. He's not doing much himself. There's no racing except Ireland.'

'He's a Bookie. He'll have it. He'll lend it you, for this. If need be, I'll stand guarantee.'

'Very good of you, Freddy, but . . .'

'You're clemmed, Percy, you have to take this!'

The Old Man bowed momentarily to the truth of this.

'No hope of two hundred, none at all.' He stood up, eye on clock, but Freddy Douthwaite would not be denied.

'I could let you have the two hundred, Percy. Of course, I'd want it back. Twenty a week, till it's three hundred?'

There was a long silence.

Freddy Douthwaite thought the Old Man was disputing it. 'I call it fair,' he said. 'I call it very fair.'

'It is,' said the Old Man. 'It is.' His eye brightened at the idea of having two hundred pounds in his hand.

Freddy Douthwaite trumped that. 'Naturally, I'd pay the two hundred to the Office in your name, Percy. You'd come with me and sign forms an' that.'

The Old Man sighed as this gate of opportunity clanged shut. 'Let me think about it, Freddy.'

'No need to think, Percy. There's many would jump at it.'

'I know that and it's good of you to tell me!'

Freddy Douthwaite put out his Park Drive. He had done all he could. There were some people you could do nowt for, nice as they were. It was as simple as that. 'I'll give you while Saturday, Percy, and then I'll have to talk to somebody else.'

'Would all this be in your name?' enquired the Old Man mildly.

'Both names,' said Freddy Douthwaite. 'Thee and me.'

'And profits?'

'We'd go fifty-fifty. Of course, it'd have to be under the counter.'

And Freddy Douthwaite laid a finger along his prominent red nose.

'I see,' said the Old Man. He did.

'Saturday,' said the other.

As he remarked once Freddy Douthwaite had gone, the front door closing with a slam, 'You know why he came to me?'

I said, 'Because he wanted to help you?'

'Because he wanted to help himself.'

One thing about the Old Man, he took me into his confidence. No other father I knew did that. My friend Jack's father would hardly tell him the time. That was recognised as proper behaviour, in Blackpool.

'How help himself?'

'Well, the Amusement Park Authorities won't allow anybody to have more than two Rides, Games or Stalls. Freddy has two already. He's got some arrangement with somebody to let a friend of his have it – to wit, me. And he'll get two-thirds of all the money.'

I thought hard. 'It's still a good offer. Isn't it?'

'It is,' said the Old Man. 'If you've been brought up as Freddy Douthwaite has, and as most of the people who work on the Park have, in two-up, two-down slum houses in Burnley or Bolton, and worked ten hours in the Mill every day of your life for starvation wages. Compared to that, getting up at nine o'clock of a morning, to go down to the Park every day, opening at midday and closing at midnight, all the time joshing and geeing up the punters, in the fresh air some of the time, and making money, sometimes very respectable money, a Stall on the Park is the nearest thing to Paradise on God's earth.'

'You aren't taking it, then?' I asked. In a way, I was a shade disappointed. The money situation was poor to disastrous, as the Old Man put it, the Dogs and Horse Racing being more or less off. 'You aren't even thinking about it?'

In reply, the Old Man looked at the clock again, put on his hat, and made for the door.

'I hate the noise of all those shrieking women,' he opined mildly. 'It goes through my head.'

And then he was gone.

That evening I went with my friend Jack down to the Amusement Park and looked at the shuttered wooden Stalls, the still and silent Rides: the Big Dipper, the Joy Ride, the Snake. I hardly ever went on the Park. I didn't care for the noise and people with silly hats and sunburnt, vacuous faces. Jack, on the other hand, loved it all, went on anything that was free, and from his earliest days had sneaked the hot, soft sweets the rock-seller used as a 'Gee' to get the punters to buy his cold, hard, gum-splitting toffee-apples and mint-rock, a shilling a bag.

As Jack had reached out and scooped the soft new toffee, the Barker had idly reached for a cane he kept for the purpose and rapped Jack painfully across the knuckles, talking on through the action. 'Not half a crown, ladies and gents, not two bob, One shilling to You!'

Jack, yelping, and sucking his hand, had cursed.

I had looked superior. I never did anything as stupid as that. Some people wondered why Jack and I got on so well. Probably for the same reason Harry Norris and the Old Man were friends. We both admired something about the other, though in the Old Man's case it only cut one way. Most of the people the Old Man admired were dead, and included Gladstone, Disraeli, the French boxer Carpentier, the footballer Billy Meredith, and the jockey Gordon Richards. And of course, all his young friends, dead in the War.

'Will any trippers come at Easter this year?' I asked.

Jack hazarded that they would. 'Unless the War starts properly, they will.'

'Then having a Stall would be a good thing.'

'Try getting one,' said Jack.

I wanted to tell him about Freddy Douthwaite and the Old Man, but I didn't. I said, instead, 'You worked for Freddy Douthwaite, didn't you?'

He had, though under age, fetching the loose wooden balls at the back of the Arcade. Jack was like his father, he had no false pride. It would never have occurred to him. Now, he had left school early and found a job in the Co-operative Butchery Department. As we walked around the quiet and shuttered Park, peeling under the early Spring sunshine, Jack told me the secrets of the Butchery Trade. He was in it because his father was a Master Baker, and the idea was that after a seven-year Apprenticeship he'd save his money and one day have a Shop of his Own.

Well, that was the dream.

Jack was the only Butcher's Apprentice in the North of England who read Evelyn Waugh.

He told me that when they went up to the Porkery to pluck the chickens for the weekend, the young apprentices threw some of the plucked or half-plucked birds through the open windows, to be neatly caught by confederates standing below, who promptly put them in the baskets of their bikes and rode off and sold them to the landladies at knock-down prices.

He told me of his Shop Manager, Cyril, a middle-aged man with a fund of dirty stories, who, come the late closing-hour of nine o'clock on a Saturday night, placed a perfectly boned sirloin of beef on the top of his brilliantined head, and softly eased his bowler hat down over it. Thus, no rival Manager or company spy could detect it and accuse him of going home with the firm's meat.

'But you take sausages home all the time!'

'Sausages, aye,' said Jack. 'We're talking about a sirloin here. We're talking about the Sunday dinner, five or six bobs' worth of meat! Of course, Meat Rationing's killed all that.'

I walked on, gazing at the huge meccano-like struts of the

Snake. It was usual for at least two people to fall off into the deep water of the Boating Pool every Summer. It was never made a fuss of, then, in case it scared people off. Later, after the War, it was made safer. I thought: everything in this place, maybe everything in the world, isn't what it seems. It all looks honest and above-board, but it isn't. There's a scam going on *everywhere*. I said this to Jack.

'Well, of course there is! Anybody knows that.'

We took a football on to the Sands and played until it was dark.

All the time I thought about the Old Man and Freddy Douthwaite and what he should do. I made up my mind to tell the Old Man he must take the Stall. It was the sensible thing to do. I felt a pang. If he did that he would be just like anybody else.

And he wasn't, was he?

Harry Norris brought his wife Rachel to the house the next night. Since Jane had died and Peggy had got married and moved to Manchester and Ted had gone into the RAF, that only left the Old Man and me.

Rachel interrupted the Old Man's efforts to make a pot of tea. It should come out, he said, as hot as Hell and as strong as the Devil, but Rachel didn't like it that way. The black strong tea was poured down the sink and fresh tea made. When ready, it was poured into the best cups, usually left gathering dust in the cabinet. It was very hot but very weak.

The Old Man gazed at it in irritation. 'Maiden's Water,' he muttered under his breath.

'Percy,' said Rachel, bossy now she was the only woman in the room, 'you should get married again.'

'I'm not divorced,' said the Old Man comfortably.

Rachel looked interested. 'Could you get together again?'

'Cat and dog,' said the Old Man.

Rachel looked crestfallen. She was wearing her best fur-stole and a coat of good melton cloth, and carried a leather handbag. She sipped her tea and nibbled a cracker biscuit (the only kind the Old Man ever ate) and looked at her husband, and said, 'Well, Harry, what is all this about?'

'Let Percy tell it.' Harry's eyes gleamed. He sat on the edge of his seat. He seemed tense, expectant, happy.

Rachel turned to the Old Man and waited.

The Old Man lit a Churchman's, crossed his legs, inhaled and said, 'Rachel, Harry has been made a splendid business offer.'

'Oh?' Rachel closed her handbag with a snap.

The Old Man wasn't deterred. 'It's a stall on the Park. It's one of the best ones. The lease runs for a year. Harry would have to be there all day. It opens at Easter, in two weeks. Shuts to Whitsun. Opens again the end of May, runs to October, the War permitting.'

'What about our Shop?' asked Rachel, startled.

'It's taking no money,' said Harry. 'You know that.'

Rachel frowned. 'I don't know anything about the Amusement Park. My family are in furs and clothing. Respectable trade.'

'Percy knows that,' said Harry, softly.

'Nothing wrong with the Park,' said the Old Man. 'It's honest work. Harry could do it, I'm sure of it.'

'Would he own it? This stall?'

'No, he'd lease it.'

Rachel looked troubled. 'What do they want for the lease?'

'Ah, well.' The Old Man let out a long sigh. 'It isn't cheap. It wouldn't be, would it? I mean, at Easter alone, he should, if the weather's decent, take, say, a hundred pounds over the weekend.'

Rachel stared at him. 'A hundred pounds?'

'That's right.'

There was a long silence. The Old Man said, 'The cost of the lease is only two hundred, so you can see it's a bargain.'

'Harry hasn't got two hundred pounds,' said Rachel.

'No,' said the Old Man gently. 'But you have.'

'Well, not to give away!'

'This is a business opportunity, Rachel,' said the Old Man. 'Harry will make maybe five hundred pounds profit over the summer. He has expenses to pay and one or two extras but he'll have three hundred in his pocket by September, I promise you.'

That meant Rachel knew nothing of Freddy Douthwaite's private deal with Harry, and never would. The Old Man, again.

'Three hundred pounds' profit?' repeated Rachel. 'From one stall?'

'Yes.'

Rachel said, 'It's my money from the family. I don't know what they'd say if I told them what it was for.'

'Then don't tell them,' said the Old Man, 'until Harry has his profit and then it doesn't matter what they say, does it?'

Rachel fiddled with her handbag, checking it was closed. 'What's in it for you?'

The Old Man looked startled by this direct question. 'Absolutely nothing.'

'Nothing?' Rachel sounded disbelieving.

'Rachel,' said Harry, 'Percy's my friend. He knew of the offer, it was made to him, but he's passing it on to me. That's the sort of friend he is.'

The Old Man smiled and said nothing.

Rachel brooded again. 'Why don't you want it?'

The Old Man considered the tip of his cigarette. 'I expect to be going in the Army.'

Said Harry, looking admiring, 'Percy's an officer. I told you!'

Rachel stood up and collected the cups. She took them into the kitchen and washed them. Then she came back into the living room. She picked up her bag. 'I'll see. Come along, Harry.'

Harry looked at the Old Man, shrugged, and followed her.

'The trouble with women,' said the Old Man, pouring himself a whisky, 'is that they think their money is their own and so is yours.'

We went down to the Amusement Park at Whitsun, not thinking about Harry Norris or anything else. Ted was home on leave and Matt, Peggy's husband, was off-shift in the Fire Service. They, as occasional visitors, loved the garish Park, and so we walked down – it took us half an hour but everybody walked then – led by the Old Man, who had still heard nothing from the War Office.

'Isn't that Harry?' asked my sister Peggy, collapsing into giggling and thinly disguised laughter.

It was. Harry still wore his homburg hat, which looked dusty, but his white coat was far too big for him. He was perspiring from the heat of the sun. It was early May and the Germans hadn't started their attack on France yet, but the weather was hot. Harry didn't notice the Old Man until he had served the last punter with Three Balls for Sixpence, and surveyed the crowd around the Stall.

'Any more for any more?' he asked politely, as if he was still in his carpet shop.

This was too much for my sister Peggy, who had to turn away giggling. I was ashamed of her.

'Hello, Mr Norris, how are you?' I asked, but Harry had turned to the Old Man. His manner was suddenly jaunty. 'Percy!'

'Harry,' said the Old Man. 'I haven't seen you for a while.'

The Old Man wasn't criticising Harry. He had said to me, walking up to the Park, that Harry was spending more time with his wife's relatives and the Jewish Community around the synagogue. He had closed the Carpet Shop. 'I don't think his wife's relatives object to him so much, now he's making a bob or two.'

'Pity. He used to like going to the Snooker with you.'

'Life goes on,' said the Old Man.

He taught me something there. In life, let go easily.

Now, he waited for Harry to speak.

'Money,' said Harry, leaning forward to miss the flying wooden balls as they crashed against the rubber Bull's Eye and the Man crashed, cursing, into the water, and the male punters roared and the women shrieked.

'Money,' said Harry. 'They Throw It At You.'

'Calais,
Next Stop
Blackpool'

Jack and I joined the Home Guard.

France had fallen. Even in Blackpool people felt a frisson of fear. The Army Service Corps drove pylons into the Seven Miles of Golden Sand, to stop German gliders landing on it, and nobody in a town devoted to gaiety laughed at the idea. The danger was so real you could smell it. People on Highfield Road talked in whispers in the shops and on the streets.

And the sun blazed down on it all.

Good weather for Tanks, the newspapers said.

For myself, I expected them any moment, partly because it was what Onkel Frank had been saying for years. Jack and I were Children of the Left and had been banging on (as they say now) at the Tory-voting Blackpudlians about Adolf Hitler for years. We had not made ourselves popular. We were nobbut lads and knew nowt. Unlike most citizens of the resort, we had read Tom Wintringham's advice on 'How to Repel the Fascist Invaders', in the *News Chronicle*. We had read Orwell too, although our devotion to Socialism was too blinkered for us to take seriously Orwell's diatribe against the Communists in Spain. Nor could we understand the substantial Pacifist movement in the Labour Party. The Old Man had a word on that. He had served in the Front-line next to a French Regiment. 'They dressed these Conchies in uniform, handed them a rifle and bayonet, and asked them for the last time, Would they fight? When they said No, the officer said, "Well, join your friends the Boche!" And threw them over the parapet into No Man's Land.' The Old Man sighed. 'That was the French, then. Now? I doubt if they have the stomach to go through all that again.'

As so often, he turned out to be right, but we didn't know that then. We believed what we read in the *New Statesman and Nation* and *Tribune*. We were just about the only people in Blackpool who read those periodicals, apart from a few old Trotskyites on the Trades Union Council. Hitler was coming, Onkel Frank had been saying for years. And here he was. 'Calais, next stop Blackpool,' said Jack.

Jack knew about the Home Guard (then called the Local Defence Volunteers) from the newspapers. He proposed we join at once and so we went along to the Porter's Lodge of the nearby Old Soldiers' Home and put our names down, as one might for a local football team. Men we knew from seeing them walking about the streets, the fathers of friends, *old* men, wearing ribbons from the last War on their jackets, like roses, were in the majority. Two men in uniform were seemingly in charge.

The Commanding Officer was Major Lees, a local Schoolmaster. His RSM was Mister Neal, who ran the OTC at the school. They were both men over fifty years of age. They were as old as the Old Man and Jack's father.

Who were not present.

Mr Neal, who knew the Old Man, asked where he was.

'He's on the Reserve,' I said.

'Has he taught you anything about using a rifle?'

'He's taught me to drill and then load, aim, and fire.'

Mr Neal was a very large man, ex-Coldstream Guards. 'You get a rifle, lad, and a clip of five rounds.'

I took the rifle. It was a Short Magazine Lee Enfield and it felt very heavy.

'Only five rounds?'

'All we've got,' said Mr Neal briskly. 'Next?'

Jack was next.

Mr Neal was, by long Army training, an acute judge of men. 'Here you are, Son.'

He handed Jack a sawn-off billiard-cue.

'What the bloody hell am I supposed to do with this?' asked Jack.

'Language to a Superior, it's a chargeable offence,' said Mr Neal, kindly. 'Can you fire a rifle, lad?'

'No,' said Jack. 'But—'

'Next,' said Mr Neal.

'Bloody Hell,' said Jack. 'I'm going to fight Fascism with a sawn-off billiard-cue! Now I've heard everything!' He added, 'The Miners in Spain rolled dynamite under Franco's tanks, y'know!'

Mr Neal digested this information.

'We ain't got no dynamite,' he said. 'Next!'

Next was Bill Squeers.

He really *was* called that, and he had medals on his jacket going back to the Boer War, including the Mons Star. He was short, very old, and grey-haired (what was left of it) and he wore glasses with a crack in them. Mr Neal surveyed him without enthusiasm.

'Hello, Bill.'

'Sar' Major.'

'D'you reckon you can fire one of these things without the kick knocking you over?' asked Mr Neal.

'I could fire one of these with me John Thomas if I had to,' said Bill, taking the rifle and hefting it. 'I fired one of these till it was red-hot at Mons.'

'Aye,' said Mr Neal, not unkindly. 'But you could see what you were firing at in them days.'

Bill said, 'I've taken a tuppenny bus-ride to get here. Do I get a rifle or not?'

Mr Neal sighed. 'Are you sure you can sight it?'

Said Bill Squeers, 'I could sight it with me cock.'

'Here y'are then.' Mr Neal handed him the Lee Enfield. 'Don't shoot yerself in the foot.'

Bill Squeers squinted and spat tobacco juice on the stone-flagged floor. 'Bloody Guardsmen,' he said, to nobody in particular. 'Bloody Parade Ground Wallahs.'

Jack, ever a rebel, took to Bill Squeers at once.

I had reservations. For one thing, he seemed to be half-blind. He squinted horribly through the cracked glasses as he surveyed the other volunteers, now crowding the small bare room. Most of them were veterans of the Great War, and looked it.

''Ow old are you two lads?' Bill Squeers asked.

'Seventeen,' we lied.

'Are you buggery.' He spat more tobacco juice on the floor. 'Yer nowt but a coupla felly-lads.'

Jack took umbrage. 'Have you read Tom Wintringham on Guerrilla War?'

'Eh?' said Bill Squeers.

'Tom Wintringham?' yelled Jack. Bill Squeers was plainly deaf as well.

'Is he frae Blackpool?' asked Bill Squeers.

'He wrote a book called *English Captain* about the Spanish War. He says we'll have to work as a Guerrilla Unit behind German lines, if they land in England. He says it's useless trying to be conventional soldiers!'

'Who does?'

'He does.'

'Who?'

'Tom Wintringham!'

'Who?'

Jack gave up. 'They know nothing here. They're useless. Look at 'em! They're all old crocks.'

It was true. We were much the youngest volunteers present. The ages twenty to forty were hardly represented at all. I said as much to Jack.

'They've all got wives at that age, if they haven't been called up already. Their wives won't let 'em join.'

'Why not?' Sometimes I couldn't follow Jack's reasoning.

'Because they don't want 'em bloody killed.'

It was then the possibility hit me that we were engaged on something very dangerous. Jack, although he talked about it, had obviously not yet taken it in at all. Once again, I had followed him into something I wasn't sure I wanted. But there was no turning back now. I had the Lee Enfield in my hands.

Mr Neal presented us all with khaki armbands marked LDV. We wound them around the arms of our sports-jackets or raincoats.

Mr Neal shouted for silence and everybody followed the example of the old soldiers and came to attention. Most people were smoking (including Jack), so they stubbed out their cigarettes in respect to Mr Neal. I was glad I had nagged the Old Man into taking me through the intricacies of rifle-drill and firing. Of course, I'd never fired a live round before, only Point Two-Two. I wondered if I'd be able to shoot a German if the gliders did land on the sands and the men in field-grey and jackboots came running out of them.

Mr Lees, a mild and scholarly man with the MC ribbon on his tunic (he, at least, had a tunic), said, 'Men, I won't swear you in or anything like that because I don't even have a form of words. Our job is to patrol the Front and keep an eye on the Sands where gliders or Airborne troops might land.'

There was an absolute, unbelieving silence.

'If they do come, then you telephone the Police and tell them as much as you can. Numbers, weapons, exactly where the Enemy is.' He hesitated. 'If you can, you resist them, but, whatever you do, get a message to the Police. Any questions?'

I found myself asking, 'Sir, why the Police?'

'Because we have no signals network as yet. The Police have. Any other questions?'

Nobody else had any questions.

Mr Neal read out the Patrols. We were on the midnight-to-four Patrol. Jack and myself and Bill Squeers. Jack said, 'Can we have a half-hour to tell our folks we won't be home tonight?'

Mr Neal looked surprised. 'Yes. But hurry back. And bring a coat. It gets parky on the Prom at three in the morning.'

'Bloody scooil-lads,' said Bill Squeers, lighting his foul old pipe. 'Off to tell their mothers.'

Jack and I went out and headed for his house. He insisted I came, as I had a calming effect on his mother, Sannah. It was needed. As soon as Jack told her what we had done, she started to cry.

'Nay, I don't know what your Father will say about it when he comes home!'

It was about ten o'clock at night now. Mr Ashworth was keeping his usual hours. No meal was kept in readiness for him of an evening. He would come in with fish and chips or cold tripe and mushy peas and chips or a hot meat-and-potato pie. Long before the Americans invented Convenience Foods, the workers of Lancashire, when women worked alongside men in the Mills, knew how to shop for instant food. Often Mr Ashworth's slice of honeycomb tripe would have been purchased at noon and remained in his back trouser-pocket, like a poultice, for ten hours or more. He always ate it with appetite, whatever its condition.

Now – Sannah dried her tears, lit a consoling Woodbine and asked, 'Will they give you food?'

Jack's reply was prompt. 'They haven't got guns, never mind grub.'

His mother sighed and rapidly cut us cheese sandwiches. 'I'll give you some as well,' she said to me, 'seeing as your father and you are on your own.'

She was kindness itself like that. I had notched up a hundred High Teas in her house since Jane had died and Jack none in mine, since the Old Man was a sparse caterer, running to a bacon sandwich for breakfast (I had lunch at work), and an apple, a banana (or two apples when bananas went on the ration) and a cream cake, plus hot, sweet tea at six o'clock.

A late supper at ten or eleven o'clock was always Gorgonzola cheese, raw onion and cocoa for him, Cheddar and no onion for me.

'Mrs Kirkham could do a lot more,' said Sannah as she buttered the sandwiches.

'She only cleans and dusts,' I said. Mrs Kirkham, a garrulous neighbour the Old Man suspected of attempting to poison his cat Smout, had offered to cook meals, but that would have obliged the Old Man to conform to set hours. His answer was no, but he paid her too much anyway, despite his suspicions about the cat.

I had told him that Mrs Kirkham had a fear of rats and the poison was probably put down for them. The Old Man, with his love of animals (we still had the four rabbits and six mice), doubted that.

'Just the same,' Sannah handed us our sandwiches, 'she could do more.'

Jack set off but she pressed a coat and scarf on him. He was the least spoilt of boys but she had almost lost him at four years old to pneumonia, and he was her favourite chick. It sat lightly on him.

We went round to see the Old Man. For once he was in, sipping a whisky and reading a newspaper. The cat Smout lay along his knee.

'Bad Do in France,' he said.

'He's going to invade,' I said.

'Doubt it. Napoleon didn't.'

'That was a long time ago.'

'Even so. It's the water. If He comes, I'll cost Him an Army Corps or two and He'll lose half His Fleet. Wonder if He wants that?'

'I don't think He thinks like that. He isn't coming Himself, like Napoleon might have.'

Jack said, 'If He does get here we'll have to do like Tom Wintringham says.'

'What's that?' asked the Old Man.

'Well! If you want to knock out a German Sentry and there's two of you, one of you keeps a gun on him from cover, and the other creeps up on him and strangles him from behind with a piece of cheese-wire.'

'Cheese-wire?' asked the Old Man, surprised.

Said Jack, 'Whichever way, he's dead. If he turns, the fella with the gun shoots him. If not, waaaaagh!'

And Jack drew his finger across his throat.

'Who is this Tom Wintringham?' asked the Old Man.

'He's opening a School at Osterly Park,' said Jack. 'He's full of stuff like that. He says we have to be Guerrillas!'

'Guerrillas?' said the Old Man thoughtfully.

'Only way,' said Jack.

'Where's your cheese-wire?' asked the Old Man.

'Haven't got any yet.'

'Well,' said the Old Man, 'what have you got?'

'A sawn-off billiard-cue,' said Jack.

'To do what with?'

'Hit Jerry on the head.'

'Seems a waste of a good billiard-cue to me.'

'I've got a rifle,' I said.

'Lucky boogr,' said Jack.

'Well,' said the Old Man, 'be careful with it. It isn't a toy.'

'We came to tell you we'll be out all night,' said Jack.

Said the Old Man, 'I'll leave the door on the latch.'

'Major Lees is there and Mr Neal asked for you,' I said.

The Old Man nodded. 'Tell him I'm waiting to hear from the War Office.'

'I did.'

'Oh, by the way,' the Old Man said, absently, 'you aren't wearing uniform and the Rules of War say that if a man isn't wearing a uniform he is a *Franc-tireur*. And the Germans are sticklers for the Rules of War.' As we stared at him, he added,

'What I'm saying is, they'd shoot you. Even if you were a prisoner.' He returned to his newspaper.

'Is that true?'

'Certainly. Ask anybody.'

Outside, Jack said, 'Your old fella is worrying about nothing, isn't he? It's all balls about shooting us, isn't it?'

'I don't know.' I didn't.

We started to walk back to the Porter's Lodge. It was dark now. I wondered why nobody had mentioned *Francs-tireurs*.

Midnight found us patrolling the South Promenade. I was self-conscious, carrying the heavy rifle at the trail. It had no sling. The few holiday-makers who had stared curiously at us as we walked over the bridge at Harrowside were long behind us. I peered over the sea-wall. The tide was out. The metal pylons gleamed in the watery moonlight.

Far across the bay, Liverpool burned.

The Germans had been bombing it for three nights now.

Above us we could hear the Dorniers taking a wide sweep for home, bombs away.

There was no life on the Promenade at all. Such visitors as there were in the town were long ago locked up in their hotel rooms. As Jack said, 'Some people will be on holiday when Hitler comes.' We had an easy disrespect for the holiday-makers. We saw so many of them.

Our Patrol was from Harrowside to Squire's Gate, a distance of about two miles of sea-front. Said Jack to old Bill, 'D'you reckon gliders could land on that sand?'

'What?' said Bill Squeers.

Jack shouted, 'Gliders? On that sand?'

Bill Squeers peered out to sea. 'Are there boats out yon?'

'Nay, bloody hell,' said Jack.

'We had boats ready to tek us off at Antwerp in the First

War,' said Bill Squeers, lighting his pipe. 'Nah, that were a War wi' some bloody sense to it, not two felly-lads walking along Prom wi' an old Sodjer an' one of them wi' a bloody billiard-cue.'

Jack debated replying but instead ran the sawn-off billiard-cue along the benches attached to the sea-wall.

Said Bill Squeers, 'What you don't want is owt to do wi' them Jerry bayonets. They have blades on 'em like hacksaws.'

'Why?' said Jack.

'To saw their way through bone if they has to.'

'Nay, bloody hell, cheer us up, you old nit,' said Jack.

'You what?'

'What's *that*?' said Jack, pointing seawards.

'I can see nowt,' said Bill Squeers.

Jack grinned and strode on, rattling his billiard-cue.

Suddenly there was a loud *bonk*.

A tramp, cocooned in newspaper, rose from his sleeping-place on a bench, holding his head and wanting to fight.

Jack was collapsing with laughter and I was no better.

'I'll fokkin kill you young buggers!' shouted the tramp, an elderly man well out of condition. 'I've a mind to *do* thee all!'

He paused as Bill Squeers put his rifle in his face.

'Nay!' said the tramp.

'Boogr off,' said Bill Squeers, 'Or'll bloody shoot yer!'

The tramp shouted, 'Who are yer, bloody Germans!' Then he was gone, into the night.

This encounter cheered Bill Squeers. 'Lazy boogr. He's probably never done a hand's turn of work in his life.'

We walked on, out of step.

'What do you do for a job?' I asked Bill Squeers.

'I'm an Old-Age Pensioner, lad.'

'Nay, bloody hell,' said Jack, in the darkness.

We made our point at Squire's Gate with the Patrol working inland, and after the other men had smoked cigarettes and old Bill had puffed on his pipe and Jack had tried vainly to hide the billiard-cue, we told them of the encounter with the tramp.

They all laughed. Nobody had any sympathy for a homeless vagrant. It was popularly accepted that his predicament was his own fault. One of the men said he had himself been on the Dole for three years. His money was seventeen shillings for himself, twelve for his wife and four shillings for each of his kids, a grand total of two pounds one shilling, Old Money. Nobody said anything. Like want and penury, unemployment had a stigma attached to it then. It was a shameful thing if a man couldn't keep his wife and family. Only in the Depressed Areas, such as Wales and Scotland and the North East, was it accepted, because there everybody was out of work.

Not now. The War had changed all that.

'Thank God for the bloody War,' said the man. 'It's got me a job.'

The older man spoke, conversationally. 'I walked to Blackpool in 'Thirty-four, looking for work!'

'Where from?' asked Jack.

'Barnsley.'

'That's a hundred miles. You walked it?'

'Every step of the way, Son.'

Nobody spoke in the freezing, deserted tram-shelter. But sympathy hung in the air. Obviously, the night and the danger brought out confidences.

'I got a job working in a hotel kitchen. Peeling spuds. Now I'm a porter.'

'Ah thowt for a minute tha was goin' to tell us tha owned

the place!' said Bill Squeers, who seemed to hear what he wanted to hear.

Everybody laughed at such an idea. Money did not move around then, hardly at all. It stayed in the hands, as the Old Man said, of them that had it.

We walked back along the Prom the way we had come.

I was earning thirty shillings a week. It was not something I ever mentioned to people. Most of them expressed surprise at such a young lad earning so much. The reason was simple. I was doing a man's job. The man who had been doing what I did now was unemployed. He had a wife and children. I had only recently discovered that. I did not like the feeling, but there was nothing I could do about it. Besides which, there were jobs now and probably the man had got one. He had been paid fifty shillings. I understood his health was bad.

I liked that even less.

As we passed the Sunken Gardens, Bill Squeers stopped. He peered into the darkness. Far below, in the stone alcoves of the Gardens, we heard voices. We listened and then peered at each other in the darkness. One of the voices was foreign.

Bill Squeers put a bullet up the spout of his Lee Enfield. He then shouted, in a surprisingly loud voice, 'Who Goes There?'

No reply in English, but a burst of words in a foreign tongue.

'It's a bloody Jerry!' said Bill.

'It can't be!'

Bill Squeers shouted, 'Advance Below and Be Recognised!'

Nothing for a long moment.

Then a torrent of foreign words.

Then a stone thrown up from below. It hit Bill Squeers in the chest. He staggered. 'Nay!'

Crack!

The bullet whipped round the Sunken Gardens. It seemed to ricochet from just about everything down there.

Neither Jack nor I saw it because we were both flat on our faces.

'Who fired?' asked Jack hoarsely.

'Bill,' I said. 'I *think*!'

Above us Bill peered down. We stood up, ashamed.

'What's the matter wi' you two scooil-lads?'

Before we could reply, a figure emerged from the alcove below. It was a man wearing what seemed like an Air Force uniform and yet not quite an Air Force uniform. He was in a state of undress. His tunic was undone and his shirt-tail was outside his trousers.

Behind him, a female voice squealed in terror.

'Nay, bloody hell,' said Jack. 'It's a Pole with a woman!'

Bill Squeers put another bullet up the spout.

We pulled him away. Then, taking an arm each, we ran him all the way back, up Harrowside Bridge, until we were almost at the Porter's Lodge, and then we stopped, breathless.

'What the hell's to do wi' thee!' demanded Bill. 'Was that a Jerry? Or what?'

'No. It was a Pole. They're our allies.'

'Our what?'

Jack shouted, 'You fired that cartridge in error! Report it when we get inside! Say you were demonstrating the rifle to me and it went off! Don't say anything about the Pole!'

Said Bill Squeers, with amazement, 'Tha's not so green as tha's cabbage-looking, lad.'

We went inside and told the story. Nobody believed us.

The Old Man didn't join the Home Guard.

They had changed the name but not much else. We had uniforms now and heavy Army boots and every man had a rifle. The rifles were American Springfields with a round foresight that made them easy to bracket an Enemy. They were clogged with thick grease when we broke them open from the wooden boxes in which they had rested since the First World War. Everybody cursed the job of wiping them clean.

At least Jack didn't have his sawn-off billiard-cue any longer.

But there was no Guerrilla training, à la Tom Wintringham. Jack took it up with Mr Neal. He had a booklet written by Wintringham, showing how to fight a dirty guerrilla war. Shooting the Enemy in the back, at night. Ambushes. Making simple Molotov Cocktails from milk bottles, rags and petrol. Fighting the Invader in groups of ten or less, striking and disappearing into the night.

Mr Neal was good-natured about it. Jack was showing an interest. That was good. A lot of people, he hinted darkly, sitting in his tiny cubbyhole in the Porter's Lodge, were in the Home Guard for the company and the beer and to get away from their wives.

'Jack lad,' said Mr Neal, 'I've read this book and it's about civil disobedience, not soldiering. There's no soldiering in it.'

'If the Germans attack us and occupy the country, what then?' asked Jack. 'We'll have to fight behind the lines!'

'You can't do that,' said Mr Neal. 'You'd be a *Franc-tireur*. They'd shoot you down like a dog. And they'd be right.'

I said, 'Sir, will they respect our uniforms, or will they think we're Irregulars?'

Mr Neal shook his head. 'I don't know. We'd have to take our chances. But if we fought in a soldierly way, then I don't think they'd treat us as Irregulars, no.'

'In a soldierly way,' repeated Jack. 'Does that mean running at them with fixed bayonets?'

Mr Neal puffed on his pipe. 'Yes. Why not?'

'Nobody in this War,' said Jack, 'up to now, has won anything charging with fixed bayonets. The Germans have a Tommy-gun to every fifth man.'

'Well, we haven't,' said Mr Neal. 'We're part of the British Army, lad, and we have the traditions of the British Army to uphold!'

'We haven't done so well up to now, have we?' asked Jack.

'I didn't hear that, lad,' said Mr Neal. 'But I can tell you, no Army will ever fight the way recommended in this book. This is for peasants and them as know nothing about soldiering. You'd do well to forget it.'

Said Jack, in defeat, pushing the booklet into his denim tunic, 'We'll be drilling when they occupy the Town Hall.'

Mr Neal ignored that, knocked out his pipe and got to his feet. So did we. The talk was over.

To me, he said, 'What news of your father? We're still very short of officers.'

'He goes to Manchester next week, for an interview and a medical.'

Mr Neal sighed. 'Pity, that. We could use him.'

On our way out we bumped into Bill Squeers. He had been demoted to Unit Cook on the strength of the Sunken Gardens Incident, and his rifle taken away from him. He did not seem to mind such summary unkindness, this being what he expected of the Army.

Bill held in his hand a bowl of steaming stew.

'Who's that for, us?' asked Jack.

'Is it buggery,' said Bill. 'It's Gordon Price's supper.'

Gordon Price was our new Commanding Officer. He was

gimlet-eyed, a disciplinarian and very bright. He was in a Reserved Occupation. He had made things hum a bit and was resented by some of the Old Soldiers.

'He's doing all right,' said Jack. The stew smelled good.

Bill Squeers stirred it with a fork. 'Yes, it's for Gordon.' He spat in the stew and stirred it again. 'Lovely fella, nobody likes him.'

'Come on,' said Jack. 'Let's go and have a pint.'

We were under age, but no publican would refuse us in uniform. Jack was already a talented drinker. I had a job to keep up with him. I'd taken him home drunk the week before and Mr Ashworth had greeted us at the door, in his stockinged feet, as usual.

'What kind of a goin'-on d'yer call this?' he had whispered, in case Sannah heard him.

Mr Ashworth had probably drunk enough for two ordinary drinkers himself that very night. But he didn't look drunk. He didn't stagger. And he had control of his voice.

Jack had none of these assets.

Putting an unlit cigarette in his mouth, he said to his father, 'I've let the peg go tonight, y'know.'

'Yer nowt but a felly-lad!'

'It's my birthday!' protested Jack.

It was. His sixteenth.

'Nay! Do right! Your *Mother*!' And Mr Ashworth's granite-like fist struck Jack in the ribs, a short but terrible blow that all but cut him in two. This was the second such punishment he had meted out to Jack in recent weeks, not against the misdemeanour itself, but against the fact that his mother might find out about it.

On the previous occasion it had been a packet of Durex under his pillow. Jack could hardly recall buying them, having drink-taken, and certainly had no possibility of using them. Nobody did, then. His father was not concerned about any of that. He was concerned that Sannah might have found them. Hence the iron fist, driven into the ribs.

'By God,' said Jack. 'He can hit you when he wants to.' Jack bore no ill-will towards his father. He never bore ill-will towards anybody.

The Dunes Hotel was full of Home Guardsmen off duty, or just going on. They looked a lot more what Mr Neal would call soldierly but, as Jack said, all we'd ever done for eighteen months was drill and march and patrol the sea-wall and look at Liverpool burning and wonder if He would come tonight, and what would we do if He did? Present Bloody Arms?

We got our beers and sat down. I yawned. I was finding doing a hard job and staying up all night on Home Guard duty well-nigh impossible. Leonard had closed his business and I had an even better job at the Vickers aircraft factory, in the sub-contracts office. It was interesting work, watching the Wellingtons grow on the Production-line all the way to the door, where the Test Pilot would take them up, and hope everything was in the proper place. The hours were long, ten a day, seven days a week. I was earning an amazing four pounds a week by now. The Old Man, patriotic though he was for himself, secretly hoped I would remain there for the duration of the War. I suppose I could have but it was really never to occur to me. Everybody I knew was in the Forces, many in the Air Force. Some were already dead.

'I'm going to miss my turn on Nights this week,' I said. 'I can't last the day if I don't sleep.'

Jack looked uncomprehending. He did a mostly physical job, sometimes in the fresh air. He didn't realise I had to have my wits about me. As usual, I had been promoted above my station, the man I was working with having fallen ill. I'd learned the details of the job quickly, because I had to. They were pleased with me and I was afraid they'd try to bar my way into the RAF by asking to keep me.

Jack had already volunteered, and hoped to go soon. He didn't care what as. I had a fear he'd end up as a Rear Gunner (a renowned short-cut to Eternity) but, as he said, 'you're all in the same kite. If it goes down it doesn't matter what brevet you've got on your chest.'

It was a simple way of looking at things.

Looking at him sitting drinking his pint, puffing on his cigarette and laughing, I had a premonition. I pushed it away. It was to haunt me for a long time.

The Old Man needed a suit for the Interview and Medical. He decided it had to be a new one.

All clothes were 'On Coupons' but the Old Man always knew the kind of people who could obtain such things. You did not have to look very far, in most bars or clubs, to find them. They just cost money.

The Old Man made his way to Fox's, the best Gentlemen's Outfitters in the town. 'No time to get anything made, d'you see,' he apologised. The idea of a ready-made suit was an anathema to him, but needs must, as he said.

The Manager at Fox's, who, inevitably, knew him, had one suit only and it was far too big. He advised against the Old Man taking it. The price was three pounds, knocked down from five on account of its size. Being flush, I offered to pay.

The Manager was still worried. 'Look, Percy. This suit

would fit a giant. Next week I should have something to fit you.'

'No good,' said the Old Man. 'I have an interview on Thursday.' It was Tuesday evening.

'I've lost most of my tailoring staff. I can't do anything for you in that time.'

The Old Man paid him with my three pounds. 'Don't worry, we'll be all right.'

We got on the tram. I was carrying the suit.

'Where now?'

'We're going to see Old Fletcher.'

Old Fletcher was an elderly tailor who worked from his house. We found him up to his neck, as he said, in uniforms. Blackpool nowadays was full of Poles and RAF recruits, billeted in the boarding-houses. Since nobody's uniform fitted first time, he was on what the Old Man said the Americans called a Bonanza!

Old Fletcher, tape around scrawny neck, in hard celluloid white collar, said as much. 'I couldn't do it, Percy, even for you.'

The Old Man rang two half-crowns down on the work-table. 'That's over and above what it costs. But I have to have it tomorrow night. I go to Manchester on Thursday morning. I'm going in the Army.'

'Nay, bloody hell, Percy,' said Old Fletcher. But the mention of the Army did it.

Old Fletcher said, 'I'll be up half the night. But here, let me tek a few measurements.' Old Fletcher paused. 'Who sold you this suit? You could get two men in it!'

The Old Man closed an eye at me.

I collected the suit next evening. The Old Man was playing Snooker.

Old Fletcher said nothing about the bill, although I could see him wondering whether or not to. So I said, 'What do I owe you, Mr Fletcher?'

'Nay, lad,' he responded. 'I'll see Percy.' His tone, nonetheless, was doubtful.

The Old Man had conjured a suit, as Jack later said, out of thin air for five shillings. He added that he had never heard of anybody tipping a tailor in advance of not paying him.

The Old Man didn't pass the Medical. It was the Feet. The Army Doctor knew he'd had Trench Feet in the First War, even had a pension for it for a while. The Doctor had told him, 'Sorry, you'd never last a route march. Pity.'

To the Old Man, who walked everywhere and wanted to go back in the Army more than anything in the world, it must have been a terrible blow. But the Army he remembered was gone, it belonged to his youth, and all the young men who had been in that Army and that War were dead. It was really a dream he had, a wanting to go back to another time, a brave, idyllic time that existed only in his memory. Of course, I knew none of that then. And he, naturally, never spoke of it or showed his disappointment in any way. People didn't.

I said, 'Well, you can always join the Home Guard.'

'Join that ragtime mob,' said the Old Man. 'Never.'

'Oh, by the way, don't forget you owe Mr Fletcher.'

'Of course I won't forget!'

The next night I went round and paid Old Fletcher myself.

The Hats

Uncle Harold, the Scotch Comic, was at the front door. I was astonished to see him because I knew he was dead.

'Don't ye know me?' he asked, irritably.

Of course I knew him. How is it possible to forget a man who could do so many things at once? At age five or thereabouts I had seen him sit in his chair in front of the fire at my Aunt Clara's house, a bald man of indeterminate age, in his shirtsleeves, sitting having his pipe, as they used to say. On his ears were clapped headphones similar to the kind young people wear in the street today. His were connected to a loop of aerial-wire that went round the picture-rail and then to a glass dome containing a cat's whisker. It was the BBC broadcasting on 210. I was allowed a listen. I remember the voices had a purity you will never hear now. Now there is always a backwash.

My Uncle Harold was usually reading a daily newspaper on these occasions, 'resting' from his labours in the few Music Halls and Clubs still requiring his services. He was also tearing up an old newspaper into a design, part of his Act, for practice.

'Why are ye no' at the school?' he would ask.

'The certificate's been Sent In,' I would protest.

'Personally,' he replied, sadly, 'I went to the High School. On the hill. No' a posh wee place like yourself.'

His humour was mordant Glaswegian, and contained such gems as, 'Ah'm wearin' ma best suit the noo; the brown one wi' the grey waistcoat and the blue trousis.' He had an excellent tenor voice and was billed as 'Harold Carlisle, the Little Man with the Big Voice'.

'His Act,' the Old Man said, 'he could perform in front of the vicar. In himself, he is a foul-mouthed, objectionable little fellow, particularly when he is in drink.'

I found these dual and conflicting signals hard to take in, so went on believing neither one. I did however once hear him say of Clara, his wife and partner in the Act, 'That woman is as thick in the heid as shite in a bottle.'

It seemed a fine statement but again I doubted its truth. My Aunt Clara seemed to me to be a jolly, cheerful woman, full of life and spirit, still good-looking despite no longer being young and no longer performing on the Music Halls. She had left Harold to his vagabond life a year before, and come to Blackpool to look after the Old Man. Newcastle had been blitzed and her house destroyed, so in a sense she had nowhere else to go.

Clara professed not to like Blackpool, but in fact thrived on the racy, cosmopolitan air of the place. She attended and won many Whist Drives, having, the Old Man swore, a photographic memory in place of brains.

'I don't know why so many people are anxious to live with me or look after me,' the Old Man complained. 'Particularly since it always seems to cost me money.'

'Aunt Clara thinks you're dead,' I told Harold at the door.

Harold waved his pipe irritably. He wore a cloth cap and

a black Civil Defence overcoat two sizes too big for him. 'I'm no' deid, as anybody can see! Is she in?'

'Nobody's in. Just me.'

'I'll stay a wee minute then.' And he strode past me and into the house.

'Jane no' here?'

'She died two years ago.'

He looked sad. 'A decent old soul. Is there such a thing as a drink in the hoose? We'll take a dram to her memory.'

I took the Old Man's whisky bottle out of the sideboard. Harold inspected it with approval. 'Ye can say whit ye like aboot Percy but he keeps a decent bottle.'

He poured himself a large glass and sat down and sipped it.

'Where are they all?'

'Aunt Clara's selling her glasses and the Old Man's at work.'

He looked astonished. 'Ye're no telling me he has a job?'

'He's working at the Air Ministry. They're evacuated here.'

'Is it a guid job?'

'He likes it.' It was true. The Old Man had found a home in the Air Force. It was his kind of thing. Male and ordered and everybody with badges of rank. He fitted easily into it. Also, many people there liked a bet and a drink. It was congenial company.

'Wasn't he on the Army Reserve?'

'He was,' I said. 'But he's too old now.'

Harold appraised me. 'Ye'll be going next.'

'Yes,' I said. I knew it too well.

'How old are ye now?'

'Seventeen.'

'Anytime now, then?'

'Yes.'

'Whit are ye goin' in?'

'The Air Force.'

He nodded his head. 'Aye. Keep oot o' the Infantry.' All the older men said that.

He looked around the room and nodded. 'Ye're in a job?'

'Yes. I've been home half an hour.'

'What kind o' job?'

'In an office.'

He nodded approvingly. 'Ye have the brains.'

'Aunt Clara's goin' to get a surprise when she sees you. She thinks you were killed by that bomb,' I said.

Harold lit his massive pipe. 'Damn near. I lay in the hospital for weeks. They let my sister know. They couldn't find Clara.'

'She came here,' I said. 'Her house is down.'

'Aye, I know. I saw it. Whit made her think I was a lump of lead?'

'Somebody in Newcastle wrote that Club in Sheffield was destroyed and everybody with it.'

He nodded. 'I was in the middle of ma act and the roof fell in. Most were killed. I gave up working after that. I'm in the Civil Defence full time noo, till I get a few bob put past me.'

'She'll be surprised all right,' I said, doubtfully.

I didn't know whether it would be a nice surprise. I thought probably not. Still, she must feel relieved when she heard he was safe, I reasoned. Had they not run away together to get married at Gretna Green because Clara was only seventeen and Edwards, as her guardian, would not give his consent to any marriage involving Harold, on the grounds that he was twenty years older than Clara, was a drinker, was On the Halls, was bald, and had no teeth.

'A formidable list,' as the Old Man said.

However, Harold had put her in his Act and they had toured the Halls as Comic and Girl for almost twenty years, until at last the bookings had faded away and Clara had given up, being no longer, as she said herself, a spring chicken. Harold, who knew nothing else, had carried on playing worse and worse dates, until his rumoured death.

Now, here he was. But he had a question.

'Why are there so many hats in this room?'

I had forgotten the Hats.

'Who do they belong tae?' asked Harold, picking one up and trying it on, looking at himself in the mirror. Although a startling shade of green, it was certainly an improvement on the cap.

'How dae I look?' he enquired.

'Very good,' I said.

He sat down. He did not take the Hat off.

I said, 'Matt, my sister's husband—'

'Aye, I know Matt.'

'He's in the Fire Service now. He's been in the Manchester Blitz. But he bought these Hats from a man in a pub and sent them here for safe-keeping.'

Harold nodded. 'He did right. How many are there of them?'

I looked round. There were Hats, in boxes, all over the house.

'A gross, all told.' There had been a gross, but they had been decreasing in number because the Old Man had been selling them, I didn't know to whom. Probably shops. All clothing was rationed and in short supply. The Hats were said to be pre-war stock. Onkel Frank had declared them knock-off.

Said Harold, 'Matt must ha' got them cheap, then?'

'I don't know. I suppose so.'

Harold nodded. 'I'm thinkin' of getting' back into the Clubs. I'm over-age for National Service.' He smoked and drank, and refilled his glass. 'I was younger than you when I went on the boards. Know how I got started?'

I waited.

'This wee boy,' said Harold, 'presents himself at the Stage Door of the Empire Music Hall in Glasgow. He asks, "Is Mister Lauder in?"

'Says the Stage Doorkeeper, "He is not. He doesn'y stay here all the time."

' "Whar is he noo?" asks the Wee Boy.

' "He's at the Station Hotel," says the Stage Doorkeeper, "until hafe-paste five, when he comes oot an' walks over here, tae save the tram-fare." '

I recalled that Harry Lauder, the most famous comic of his day, made a thing of his meanness. He had once asked Isaac Henderson for a sixpenny plate of prawns on the house, and had failed to get it.

Meanwhile, Harold was still talking.

' "What's the Station Hotel?" asks the Wee Boy. The Stage Doorkeeper tells him.

'Well now, at five-thirty Harry Lauder came out of the hotel. The Wee Boy presents himself to Lauder.

' "Are ye Harry Lauder?"

'Lauder peers at the Wee Boy in his jersey and donkey-fringe. "Aye, I am. Whit d'ye want?"

' "Tae carry your bag to the Theatre."

' "Whit dae ye want to do that for?"

' "I'm wantin' in."

' "Ye're wanting in the Theatre?"

' "Aye."

' "What are ye wantin' in the Theatre for?"

' "I want tae be a Comic when I grow up. I hear ye're the best comic in the world and I want tae see ye."

' "Ye do?"

' "Aye."

'Lauder regards the Wee Boy. "And what part of Glasgae do ye come from?"

' "I dinny come from Glasgae."

' "Where dae ye come frae, then?"

' "Kircoddy." That is the way they pronounce Kirkcaldy in Kirkcaldy,' said Harold in an aside.

' "Ye came all the way on the train frae Kircoddy tae see me?" asks Lauder of the Boy.

' "I didn'y come on the train," says the Wee Boy.

' "Then hoo did ye get here?"

' "I walked it."

' "Kircoddy is thirty miles frae Glasgae!"

' "Aye. I know it," says the Wee Boy.

'Lauder hands the Wee Boy the bag. "Well, ye'd better tak' aholt o' the bag and I'll see whit ah can do. Ah'm no promising anythin', mind ye!"

'That Wee Boy was me,' said Harold Carlisle. 'Not my real name, of course. That was Blair. Carlisle had a wee bit more class about it.'

'What happened then?' I asked.

Said Harold, 'I saw Harry Lauder that night, from the front row of the Stalls, I ate the biggest beef-sandwich in Glasgow, and I was on the train home with a ten-shilling note in my hand after the First House was over!'

Harold lit his pipe. 'Years later, I heard that Lauder told

everybody backstage, "There's a wee laddie out the front who's walked all the way frae Kircoddy to see me the night!" '

It pleased him more than a Command Performance, said Harold.

But there was only one Lauder. Everybody else was a copy. Even Will Fyfe. Even Harold. Despite the reviews and the picture of him in his kilt and sporran. I had once seen him in Panto at the Grand, Byker, and thought him magnificent. Of course I had only been four at the time.

So, here he was, sitting there, on the sofa, wearing one of the gross of Hats that had arrived by rail two weeks before.

'It's no' a bad Hat,' said Harold, reading my thoughts. 'Will Percy miss it?'

'Probably not,' I said.

'I'll settle up wi' him when I see him.'

'When will that be?' I asked, uncomfortably.

He consulted a large steel pocket-watch, remarking, 'I'm one of the few Comics who has a watch at the end of his watch-chain.' He added, 'Look, I'll tell ye whit I'll do. Tell Clara I'll meet her in Yates' Wine Lodge at Talbot Square at eight o'clock tonight.'

'Where are you staying?' I asked.

'I'll find somewhere.'

'And that's all?' I said.

He nodded and put his cap in his pocket. From another pocket he took the *Daily Herald*. It was a wartime edition, only four pages. 'You used to like this when you were a wee laddie.'

Deftly he folded the paper, then tore holes in it. Then he pulled it wide.

It was transformed into a row of paper dancing-girls.

'That's very good,' I said.

'I hae ma Scrap Book wi' me – ma little yin.' He took from an inside pocket of his Civil Defence greatcoat a small, stiff-bound album of the kind you could buy in Woolworth's. He flipped it open. It contained many gummed-in, yellowing newspaper clippings. He unfolded one or two. They spoke of good weeks at Dundee and Rothesay on the Clyde and at the Glasgow Empire, written by forgotten journalists and watched by now dead audiences, or audiences anyway that now watched James Cagney and Clark Gable. The British Working Class was becoming Americanised, a process that has never stopped. Harold Carlisle belonged to a strictly British art, that of Music Hall, and, as the Old Man remarked, it was dead as Crippen. Harold and his Scrap Book belonged to a glorious past, of great tuneful songs and cynical working-class Comics, now all gone. The son of a Jute Mill worker, he had for a time seen his name in lights, had known and got drunk with the most illustrious performers of his day. Now he was wearing a Civil Defence overcoat and one of the dubious Hats. I watched his cocky little figure waving farewell along the avenue, and I felt a pang.

Even at seventeen, sometimes one thinks of people other than oneself. Not for long, of course.

I resumed my studies (I was taking a Correspondence Course, where the Invigilators were forever accusing me of copying stories) and waited for Clara and the Old Man to arrive. This they did, almost together, at around six o'clock.

Clara, known as Tickle to the entire family, was first; bursting in, full of vim and vigour, as the Old Man said, a total extrovert, a thick winter coat wrapped round her, tam-o'-shanter on head. She feared nobody and had recently stopped a Coalman in the street and demanded a bag of coal from him. Not knowing her, he refused. Coal was on the ration. So she told him one of Harold's jokes: 'Did you hear the one about the Coalman in the Black Out? He was delivering to the top floor and he thought, my God, this bag's heavy. When somebody switched the light on, he found he had the horse by the ears!'

The coalman gave her a bag of coal, price two-and-six-pence. And whipped up his horse and jogged on.

'The woman,' said the Old Man, 'has more neck than a goose.'

I debated telling her that Uncle Harold had called, but found it difficult to interrupt her flow of words, all delivered at machine-gun speed.

'I told Mr Cowan that I wanted the glasses delivered to Top Farm, Preesall, and he sent them to Lower Top Farm, so now I've got to go all that way out on the bus tomorrow and get them and take them to the right place.'

Mr Cowan ran an opticians' firm selling spectacles. He was a middleman who had a cousin in Manchester who *was* an optician. He was a kindly man and considered Clara a gem. 'She could sell you your own shoes while they were still on your feet,' he said, fondly, adding, 'I've told her she can come and cook for me anytime. Young man, look for a wife who can cook and has a business-head.' He further advised me: 'And always have a dowry ready for a daughter. People say it doesn't matter any more, but believe me, it still does, it gives the young woman what they call status.'

I had no idea what Mr Cowan was talking about. But he always gave me advice like that.

Clara, on the other hand, lived entirely in the here and now. Yesterday was over, tomorrow wasn't here yet, so why worry about either of them?

Now, still wearing her hat, she proceeded to produce hot

vegetable soup from a huge iron pan in the kitchen, on which the skull of a sheep floated. The bread to go with it was home-baked. Clara, as a young girl on the Music Hall circuits with Harold, had once served him a salad. His response was instant.

'Away wi' this rabbit food, woman!'

And he had sent her home to Kircoddy to learn how to cook. Her repertoire was not large but it was inviting. Like Jane before her, she made her own bread. I hardly tasted 'Shop' bread at all, until I went to the War.

Hardly anybody bakes their own bread nowadays. They don't know what they are missing.

By the time she had set the table, the Old Man had arrived home. There was no Horse-racing, except in Ireland. The Old Man's salary, which was not bad, didn't go far for some-body with his tastes, but as there was now no racing at the local Dog-track, he had to be content with the unknown Irish horses and the card-school at his Office. With the sudden full-employment of Wartime, there was a lot of loose money around and nothing much to spend it on. So mug-punters abounded. Almost everything was rationed, including cloth-ing and food.

None of that made any difference to the Old Man. Wearing one of the Hats, I noticed, he took from his overcoat pocket a piece of butter wrapped in greaseproof paper about the size of an average brick. Clara, who loved her food, shouted, 'That's two months' ration for six families!'

'Thirty bob,' said the Old Man, 'from Andy the Greek who has the café. I got the same for the Furniture Man.' This was my brother Ted's father-in-law, who had done well out of both Wars. He was reputed to have buckets full of paper money swinging gently under the floorboards. He did not trust Banks. He was also a diabetic. 'Thought he'd want the butter,' said the Old Man. 'So I took it round to him. He wouldn't pay thirty bob for it, he said the price was ridiculous.' He sighed. 'It wasn't that the man wouldn't pay. He couldn't bring himself to pay thirty shillings for butter. It wasn't in him.'

'What did you do with it?' asked Clara, in wonder.

'Gave it to him,' said the Old Man. 'What else?'

'But you're thirty shillings out of pocket!'

'Won't be the first time.' The Old Man applied himself to his soup, which was the sort of quick food he liked, since it didn't hold up his life.

I waited until we had eaten before I told them.

'Aunt Clara,' I said, carefully, 'I have some news for you . . . First, Harold Carlisle isn't dead.'

Clara just stared. She hadn't taken her tammy off yet.

'Second, he was here an hour or so ago. He was injured in that air raid but he's been in hospital and he says he's all right now.'

Clara still stared.

'He's hoping to see you at eight o'clock tonight in the bar at Yates' Wine Lodge.'

Clara breathed out. 'The Little Bugger!'

'Oh,' I said. 'And one other thing. He said to tell you he's doing rightly.'

'Doing rightly,' said Clara. 'He'll never do rightly while he has a hole in his arse.'

'And,' I said to the Old Man, 'he took a Hat.'

The Old Man nodded. 'He would.' He did not seem surprised at the news.

If Clara was, she didn't show it, but she spent a long time getting herself ready. Finally, with the last layer of powder and a change of hat, another Tammy, red this time, and an ancient fur wrapped round her neck, she exited into the night.

'I have no idea,' said the Old Man, as if answering his own question, 'what will be the outcome of that.'

He was probably worrying what might happen if Clara went off with Harold. It would leave us without a House-keeper and Cook, for a start. The Old Man always thought a number of moves in front.

I told him about the telegram. It had arrived just before Harold the Comic.

He went pale and still. Ted was in the RAF.

I looked at the form. 'It's from Matt. He's coming tonight.'

'Matt?' He looked relieved and concerned at one and the same time.

'Yes. He must have got leave. It says late tonight.'

The Old Man was reflective.

'How many Hats,' he asked, 'do we have left?'

I went round the house collecting and adding up the Hats. The Old Man came with me, though all he did was talk about Clara and Harold. 'Of course, the whole thing was your Grandfather's fault. He had money, he was from a good family – the Priors were watch and clock-makers going back to 1700 and before; they have models in the British Museum. Yes, the Prior's of Nesbit, famous family . . . Your Grand-father was the first son not to go into the family goldsmith's and silversmith's business. Your great-grandfather had a sil-versmith's business in London, died in Greenwich.'

I was counting the Hats. 'Twenty-seven . . .'

'My father went as a Purser on the old Pacific and Orient, saved his money, made a lot buying cheap sheep in China and selling them dear in Japan. Got rich doing it.'

'How, if he was only a Purser?'

Thirty-two Hats . . .

'Because he was a Chief Purser by then. Put the hold containing the sheep in the name of Smith.'

'Well, Japan's changed since then. Onkel Frank says they'll come in the War on Hitler's side.'

Thirty-nine Hats . . . We went into the spare room.

'Possibly. In those days it was feudal. Your grandfather had to go to the Chamberlain of the Japanese Court to get permission to bring out the team of Jugglers and Dancers. Spoke some Japanese, which helped. They performed in front of Queen Victoria.'

Forty-one Hats? Was that all?

The Old Man said, 'Then he took the troupe around the Music Halls. Forgot his hotels and hydros. He'd made money but now he wanted fame. When the Japanese troupe went home he got the plans passed for the Empire, part-built it, and lost his backers. Result, instant ruin, since he paid his creditors all he had.'

I found a Hat underneath a bed. Forty-two.

'Why did he lose his backers?'

'Newspaper fellow wrote a piece saying that a Music Hall in the centre of Newcastle had no chance and he personally wouldn't put a thousand farthings in it, never mind a thousand sovereigns.'

I couldn't see another Hat anywhere.

The Old Man said, 'Killed him. Dropped dead in the street on his way to meet his creditors. There you are, there's a lesson in it.'

I waited for the lesson but there was no more.

'Your grandfather married two beautiful women,' said the Old Man, idly. 'Both drinkers.'

I said, 'I can't make it more than forty-two Hats.'

The Old Man said, 'I suppose we'd better get them all downstairs, then.'

I carried them down into the kitchen and put them in their boxes on the kitchen table. There seemed a lot of them, but not as many as I'd thought.

'Where have the missing hundred gone?' I asked.

The Old Man said, 'After your grandfather died it was every man for himself. Frank and I got jobs collecting rents. Edwards became a Bookie. Clara was with some friends, ran away and married Harold Carlisle. Pity about her, she had no education really, nothing to make her a lady.'

'What are we going to do with the Hats?'

Said the Old Man, 'But she seems happy enough. Never knew anything better, y'see?'

'The Hats?' I said.

'A Councillor of the city, your grandfather. A large house in Leazes Terrace. Everything. And it all went, you see?'

'What about the Hats?'

The Old Man sighed. 'You go round and see Harry Budd and ask him if he'll run us out to Frank's house.'

'Now?'

'Of course now. It's eight o'clock.'

'Does the time matter?'

'Certainly it does.'

I could not see why, but I went out and walked round to Harry Budd's house. He came to the door in his shirtsleeves and said he would get his employer's car from the garage and ready to use in quarter of an hour. It would cost five shillings, payment in advance.

I said that would be all right.

Harry Todd did not get the five shillings.

He got a Hat.

Onkel Frank was surprised to see us. He came to the door, pulling the Blackout curtain back to allow us in. Harry Budd and I staggered in under the bulk of the Hats. We took them upstairs and Onkel Frank piled them into a spare room. Harry Budd and I went downstairs and took a cup of tea with Florrie, now bespectacled and domesticated, who was listening to 'ITMA'. So we listened, too, out of politeness.

The Old Man and Onkel Frank came downstairs.

Onkel Frank put his coat on in the hall. 'Just popping out with Percy,' he told Florrie.

She nodded, as if relieved. Onkel Frank wouldn't listen to 'ITMA'. More likely Beethoven, or, if he was feeling cheerful, Mozart.

We all got into the car. I sat in front with Harry Budd.

'Wheer to, Percy?'

'Back home, please, Harry.'

Harry drove us through the darkened streets. Harry was in a War Factory and only drove for his employer part-time. Somebody had got a pot of yellow paint and daubed it on Harry's front door. 'Y.B.', it had read, for 'Yellow Bugger'. A number of other youngish men had suffered. Harry appeared unaffected. Like most people in Blackpool, he was an urban peasant, removed from the soil and the mill by one generation. He did nowt for nowt and Army pay did not attract him.

Unlike the Old Man, who was patriotic for all the wrong reasons. He believed one Englishman was as good as ten foreigners. But only two or three Germans, for whom he had a high regard, having fought them hand-to-hand in the Trenches. Onkel Frank was a militant pacifist.

'Militant for Other People,' said the Old Man, 'Pacifist for himself.'

218

As we reached the house we saw a car parked outside. It was Matt's. Somehow Matt always had a car, however decrepit. This one had cost him the eight pounds he had put down on a sewing-machine. That was when he was working, selling sewing-machines two years before. He had put it down on the Hire-Purchase form in Marthaann's name. She had given him the car, as she was buying another, believing the sewing-machine to be hers. Not until they asked her for the next instalment had she realised what had happened. Relations had been strained ever since.

Matt was immensely popular with the rest of the Family. He liked a bet, which endeared him to the Old Man, who denied encouraging him, declaring, 'I never encouraged Matty to go to the fokkin Dogs,' a plain and obvious false-hood, since they commonly shared a shilling taxi together to the Dog-track.

My sister Peggy, in short, had married her father.

And bemoaned it a great deal. The while loving Matt to pieces, as they say nowadays.

He was in his shirtsleeves, sound asleep in a chair, when we went in. His white shirt was blackened by soot and his hands looked raw. His face was red from the heat of the fires burning in the Northern cities. He had watched firemen at Liverpool Docks standing with hosepipes in the grain ware-houses. One minute they were there, the next they had disap-peared into the grain, beneath which terrible fires burned. He had driven unknowingly over unexploded bombs. He had been promoted, he said, waking up, and taking a drink from the Old Man. Peggy was all right, he said, he'd just come to get the Hats, he'd found a buyer for them.

'The Hats?' echoed the Old Man.

'What Hats?' queried Onkel Frank, in the genuine puzzlement of the semi-deaf.

'I'll just put a cup of tea on,' said the Old Man, taking me by the arm into the kitchen and leaving Onkel Frank and Matt, still blinking the sleep from his eyes, in the front room.

In the kitchen he said as he filled the kettle, 'Er, one thing, slight problem, no need for you to get involved, but . . . those Hats never arrived.'

'But they did! They're at Onkel Frank's!'

'It's a little more complicated than that.' The Old Man meant he had sold the missing Hats.

I said, 'I'm not party to this. I'm going to study in my room.'

The Old Man looked relieved. 'Good idea, stick in.'

I went upstairs and studied for an hour, and then got into bed. I slept the sleep of the young and wakened early, round seven. I went downstairs and found Matt putting on his heavy black fireman's jacket.

'The Old Man says the Hats got lost in the Blitz,' he said. 'They never got here?'

I said nothing, but looked volumes.

'I wouldn't mind,' said Matt, 'but both he and Frank had the bloody things on their heads while they swore they'd never arrived.' He put on his peaked cap and shook my hand. 'Good luck and God Bless.'

I saw him to the door.

'Oh,' I said, 'did Clara come in? Did she say anything about Harold?'

Said Matt, 'Seems they had a few drinks, got to arguing, and parted on Fighting Terms. Like the old song.'

Matt got into his eight-pound car and drove away to the Blitz.

I recalled the Music Hall song:

> 'She was a sweet little Dicky Bird
> Tweet tweet tweet, she went
> Sweetly she sang to me
> Till all my money was spent.
>
> But she went Off Song
> We parted on Fighting Terms
> She was One of the Early Birds
> And I was One of the Worms.'

I knew the words because it was one of the Old Man's favourites.

I went inside and closed the door. Another day of the War was beginning.

The End
of Something

Jack was wounded in the Summer of 1942.

He was only eighteen, and his first thought was that he would never play cricket again if they took his leg off.

So, half-delirious and in great pain he shouted at the surgeons to save it. So they did.

As his best friend I had the job of taking his mother Sannah to the hospital. At the last moment, the Old Man elected to come too, although he hated hospitals. We went on the bus from Blackpool to Liverpool and then took a local bus out to Speke Hospital. It took five hours. Liverpool had been blitzed repeatedly and there were ruined buildings everywhere. A pall of dust hung over everything.

Sannah did not cry any more. 'It's all right,' she reassured the Old Man as we got on the bus. 'I'm done wi' crying.' The worst, or almost the worst, had happened, and that could be faced. She'd faced it before, when Mr Ashworth had been blown up during the First War. It was simply another dose of the same.

Jack was conscious, but only just. There was a big cage over his legs. He'd had several operations already. The ward was full of wounded men, all very young. They lay very still, sated with morphine. I don't remember thinking about it happening to me.

Nobody did. You locked the thought away.

The Old Man hailed the harassed Ward Sister, asking her about Jack's condition. A veteran of these sorts of occasions in the previous War, he still took it worse than I did.

'What does she say, Percy?'

The Old Man took Sannah's arm. 'What they told Harold yesterday. He's going to be all right.'

'But will he be able to walk?'

'Of course he will.'

Sannah nodded and sat at the bedside and took Jack's hand. I sat at the other side.

The Old Man went around the ward, talking to the young men in the beds. I knew he hated doing it because he hated any form of suffering, but he felt it was his duty. He still had the instincts of an Officer.

Jack whispered to me. 'Keep out of it.'

'I can't,' I said. 'I go next week.'

'Good luck, then.' He closed his eyes and lay still.

'It's the morphine,' Sannah said.

We left after half an hour, and got the bus back. We hardly spoke at all. There was nothing to say.

I wondered when, if ever, we would play cricket again together. All the blazing Summer of 1940 I had played cricket, jumping up to go in first, and bowling too. So many men were Territorials, now embarking for the Far East. The War was looking like a long one.

Onkel Frank said, 'The longer it lasts the better our chances. In my view, we are still Outsiders.'

'Outsiders be buggered,' said the Old Man. 'We'll see them off. It'll just take time.'

It was what everybody was saying then.

Little had happened to our lives, yet a lot had. The Old Man, of course, had his RAF job, working as an Administrative Clerk, whatever that was. The work suited him very well because he was with men in uniform, something he understood. Blackpool was an RAF Recruit Training Centre and needed huge office staffs to look after it. The Old Man had now obtained a post attached to the Entertainments Section, and found there kindred spirits, men who cared little for conventional behaviour (usually musicians and producers in civil life), and who often liked a bet.

This unit put on concerts at the vast Winter Gardens Theatre every Sunday night. Stars of Radio (the equivalent of today's Television Celebrities) appeared, in the flesh. Also Singers, Operatic (of whom the Old Man approved) and Popular, of whom he disapproved. Brought up on a diet of Light Opera, Gilbert and Sullivan, the great classical singers like Caruso and popular ones like John MacCormack and Dame Clara Butt, he had contempt for the Crooners of the day, particularly Bing Crosby. 'The man,' he said, '*groans.*' He added, 'Of course, he is an Irishman and possibly that explains it.'

'He's an American,' I said.

'The fellow has an Irish name, therefore he is Irish. Never take any notice of what people say they are. Look at their name.'

Of course, in a way he was right. Bing Crosby's forebears were Irish and he lived an Irish private life, though none of us knew that then. It is an odd theory but not so odd when you think about it, like so many of the Old Man's ideas.

The Greyhound Stadium was closed now, the animals put

down, the staff gone into the Army, the grass growing long over the track.

There was plenty of Black Market money about in Blackpool. Some people called it the Black Market capital of England. The Old Man did not take any part in it, considering it unpatriotic. He was not above getting a bit of extra butter or sugar or whatever, if it was offered to him, but he made no profit from it. He considered that part of his War Effort.

Aunt Clara showed no sign of leaving. We were eating well again. The Old Man was being taken care of, his shirts washed, his collars impeccable, his finances steady for the first time in years. Or as steady as they could ever be. He was still playing a lot of cards. All over the country, men turned to cards in a way they had not done since Edwardian times. In air-raid shelters, on airfields, in factories, and even the Front Line, a man who could play a good hand of cards could make money.

The Old Man could play a good hand of cards. He had been known, in his Army days, as Tin Arse, for his marked reluctance to try any risky gambits. Now, at the Headquarters of the RAF, on Blackpool Promenade, he sat in a lunch-time school of high bettors and more often than not walked out with their money. Where he was a risk-taking gambler with every other game, at cards he was patient, studious and prudent.

When I asked him why that was, he answered, 'Because when I was in the Army I had no private money and I knew I couldn't afford to lose, so naturally I applied myself.'

'You liked the Army too much to risk it?'

'Of course. That is what I am saying.'

On the morning I went off to the War we ate breakfast in

silence, watching the clock. He said, sipping hot, sweet tea: 'The thing is, when you go into the Air Force you do what they tell you. Expect a hard time as a recruit. It's soon over.'

'I've done plenty of square-bashing in the Home Guard. I should be all right.'

'Yes, but they've got you twenty-four hours a day from now on. For how long nobody knows.'

'No,' I said. Nobody did know. Ten years was Onkel Frank's guess. Well, it was possible. Anything was possible.

'You've had your teeth fixed, that's one good thing.' The Old Man, ever practical where the military life was concerned, had advised me to have a dental check-up before I went in, to spare myself from Forces' dentists. 'Fellow at Oxford had me on the floor, knees on my chest, to get one of my back teeth out. I was serving with two dentists, who were going not as dentists but as infantrymen, and they said this fellow was a butcher. Only tooth I ever had out.'

'What happened to the dentists?'

'Killed together first day in the Line.'

'Go on, cheer me up!'

'Well, you asked.' The Old Man pondered. 'As to Religion, put yourself down as Church of England!'

'But I don't know the Creed or anything!'

'Won't matter. If you're Something Else they'll make sure you go to the services. As C. of E. they won't bother!' He lit a Churchman's. 'As to money, I have a fiver here to be used only in emergencies. Put it in your Pay Book and forget it.'

I took the huge flimsy in my hand. I'd never had a fiver in my pocket before. Life was certainly exciting.

'As to women . . .' said the Old Man.

I waited. I hoped he wouldn't go on. He didn't.

'Nothing I need tell you there, I don't suppose?'

'No.'

'Good.' He looked relieved.

I consulted my watch, given to me by the people in the office. The Old Man said the inscription on it, *Best of Luck, Allan*, was a pity. Cut the value to half if you tried to sell it, or pawn it.

'It's a *present*!' I said.

'Just an observation.'

I had a new silver cigarette case in my pocket, a present from Marthaann. It too was inscribed with my initials. It contained twenty Churchman's, courtesy of the Old Man. I didn't really care for smoking but it was expected of a young man then.

Aunt Clara had a packet of sandwiches for me and tears were in her eyes as she kissed me. For once, she was lost for words.

At the door, the Old Man took my case and despite my protests, carried it to the Railway Station. There were several other young men, one or two of whom I knew. We were all going to the RAF Centre at Padgate. They, too, were accompanied by fathers and friends, all being falsely cheerful and noisy. There was no crying or anything like that because nobody had brought their mothers.

When the train puffed in, with a cloud of hissing smoke, we all piled into the same compartment. Nobody told us to do it. We just did it.

I shook hands with the Old Man. Our relationship, I knew, would never be quite the same again. We would never again be together in quite the same way, but that, as he would say, was life.

'Take care of yourself,' he said. 'Drop a line when you can.'

'Yes, I will.' I wanted to say a lot more but of course I couldn't. I wanted to say how much he had taught me and how grateful I was for it and the hundred other things a son wants to say to a father he loves, but never can. Or couldn't, then.

I stood at the window leaning out, as the shaming tears blotted out his spry figure, the cigarette burning unheeded in his hand, hat slanted on head, his collar white and gleaming, the regimental tie correctly knotted, a figure that called to mind only one word.

Gallant.

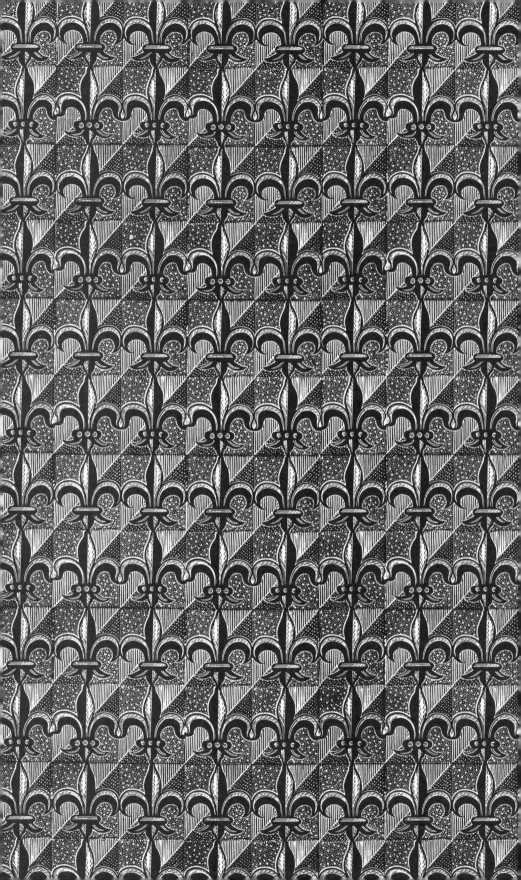